A Measure of the Soul

Other titles published by EPRINT Publishing:

A Death in the Family by Caroline Dunford
Missing Link by Elizabeth Kay
Spectacles by Pippa Goodhart
This Fragile Life by David Webb

About the author:

Stephanie Baudet was born in Cheshire and brought up in Australia and New Zealand. She returned to England in 1967 and now lives in Buckinghamshire. She is the author of about 30 children's books and teachers' resources. Stephanie loves to visit schools. She presents a flexible mix of reading and writing workshops and interactive games to help children explore different aspects of story construction. *A Measure of the Soul* is her first novel.

A Measure of the Soul

—Stephanie Baudet—

PRINT
PUBLISHING

Published in Great Britain in 2009 by EPRINT Publishing
Blackburn, Lancashire
www.eprint.co.uk

A CIP record for this work is available from the British Library.
ISBN 978-1-905637-89-8

Typeset in Great Britain by Educational Printing Services Limited,
Blackburn, Lancashire
Printed and bound in Great Britain by CPI Cox & Wyman,
Reading, Berkshire

True strength is not a measure of the body,

but a measure of the soul

Anon.

Dedicated to all victims of war

one

Harriet picked up the newspaper from the hall floor and glanced at the front page. August the first. Who would believe it was four years almost to the day since this terrible war had started? So much had happened. If only it were possible to turn back the clock. Four years ago her brother Alex had been a newly qualified doctor looking forward to a career in medicine like his father. Four years ago their father had not yet been diagnosed. Now he was dying slowly and she wouldn't wish that upon anyone, that waiting for death which crept up so slowly and inevitably.

She could hear him behind her, his footsteps feather light, his once heavy frame which had bounded down the stairs was now ponderous and unsteady like a young child's. This morning, though, she detected something that could hardly be called a spring in his step but which surely denoted a good day. She'd learnt to gauge his health by the minutest signs, they were far more telling than his answers to the question. But that was father, and she knew that she herself would probably be the same in these circumstances. God forbid that ever would be, though she knew that there was a strong possibility. However, she wouldn't dwell on that point.

She walked to the doorway of the surgery and stared into the room as if preoccupied with her plans for the day, tying her apron strings. She relived, as she did most mornings now, those days gone by, but nothing could bring them back. She'd been restless then, straining at her woman's bonds, antagonistic, wanting her freedom. Now she wished with all her heart that she could go back to that peaceful time.

She felt a hand on her shoulder.

'Good morning, Harriet.' His voice was quieter than it used to be too. No, not quieter, he had always had a soft voice with more than a hint of his native Scottish, but it was weak now and had a slight quiver in it that had certainly never been there before. She turned to face him and smiled and kissed the gaunt cheek, feeling the hollowness beneath her lips. She no longer had to reach up to kiss him, he was stooped and grey and had aged ten years in the last twelve months.

'How are you, Father?' she asked, as always trying to put an optimistic edge to her voice.

There was a fractional hesitation before he answered. 'Not too bad. I had quite a good sleep. Only the thirst woke me up as usual, but I've come to a decision, Harriet. I'll tell you at breakfast. Open up the surgery first.'

She could feel his eyes on her as she stepped into the room, although she knew he could no longer see her clearly. It was gloomy except for a fierce ray of sunshine which was forcing its way through a crack in the heavy velvet curtains at the tall bay windows.

Harriet pulled the cords as she had done every morning for as long as she could remember and the curtains swished open, letting in the summer sunshine and exposing the splendour of the room. It had been an excellent choice for a doctor's consulting room. Apart from the good London location, this room had decided her father to buy the house way back when he'd just qualified and before she was born. It was large, light and airy with a huge leather-topped oak desk and burgundy leather matching chairs. The curtains were burgundy too, a rich red wine velvet stretching almost from the high Victorian ceiling to the floor.

A large fireplace dominated the wall behind the desk, iron fire box set with newspaper and coal ready for the touch of a match, and above it a Turner print, wispy and ethereal.

'It's going to be another hot day, Father,' Harriet said, reaching to tear a page off a calendar bearing a picture of the Yorkshire Dales. 'It's the first of August,' she added, 'how much longer is this war going to last? Do you remember after it started they said it would be over by Christmas?' She laughed, humourlessly. 'Now here we are four years later, nineteen eighteen . . .' she looked up and caught the fleeting look of pain on her father's face. Then he turned and began to shuffle towards the kitchen.

'It's got to end soon,' she commented, softly, to herself as much as anything. 'Then Alex will be home again. In no time at all he'll be taking over this practice, you'll see.' She knew it was all pretence and that he knew it too. If his son Alex survived the war, he may well take over the practice, or start it up again, as their father had been unable to work for a year now. But they both knew he would never see that day.

One of the desk drawers was slightly open as one earpiece of a stethoscope was jamming it, preventing its closure. Harriet opened the drawer fully and stared at the instrument, knowing that she had dusted in here yesterday as usual and left everything tidy. Even though she knew that her father often came in here to reminisce, the poignant picture which arose in her mind of him putting on the stethoscope brought tears to her eyes. She picked it up and fingered it lovingly, remembering the numerous times when she was a child that he'd let her listen to her heart, and his, and Alex's – yes Alex's. Alex's before he was born. Alex's fluttering foetal heart in their mother's womb. Alex, whose emergence into the world to begin his life, had ended that of their mother.

'What are you doing?' her father asked from the passageway.

She replaced the stethoscope quietly. 'I'm coming, Father. Let's go and have breakfast.'

She looked round the room and shivered despite the warm day. There was a musty unused feeling even though day after day, she went through the same ritual, of opening it up. It was a sham. Keeping the surgery as it was, all ready for use as if Doctor Alfred Baker was about to open his doors to patients as he had done every morning for twenty years. A heavy wooden filing cabinet stood beside the fireplace, once chock-full of patient's record cards, patients who had by now found another physician, reluctantly maybe, but unavoidably. He'd struggled on, weakened and emaciated from the ravages of diabetes, long after he should have stopped.

Harriet caught up with him and took his arm. 'Are you feeling hungry this morning?'

She looked into his face as they entered the kitchen and she could feel how much he needed her support now with the condition of his foot obviously worsening.

He smiled at her and she was reminded of a grinning skull, for that's all his face was now. A skull covered with skin. Only his eyes remained really alive, they had not changed. They were deep blue and full of humour. Thank God he had not lost that.

'That's what I want to talk to you about,' he said, limping ahead of her to the kitchen.

'You must let me look at that foot,' she said, noting his awkwardness, but he shook his head.

'I can deal with it, Harriet.' It was what he always said. It was to protect her, she knew, not because she wasn't capable. She'd been helping him in his surgery ever since she could remember and was more than able to dress a wound. But this was no ordinary wound, this was advanced gangrene. Despite the heavy bandaging she could always smell it. The putrid odour of rotting flesh pervaded the house despite her liberal and frequent sprinkling of lavender water. They rarely spoke of it except for her offers to dress it but he'd never even let her see it. By the way he walked now she wondered if he had any toes left at all.

'I've decided,' he said, lowering himself onto a kitchen chair, 'to give up the diet.'

Harriet caught her breath and felt her heart plummet. This decision had been inevitable but now it had come she felt a sudden panic. No, please Father . . . she couldn't bear the thought of him not being here.

'Look at me,' he said, waving his hand to indicate his thin body. 'We all know there is as yet no cure for diabetes, and no way of even controlling it. Diabetes can be a death sentence and we've known that from the start. For the little time I have left I'm going to try and enjoy my food.'

Harriet felt tears welling up and blinked them away, turning to put the kettle on the gas so that she needn't think of what he'd said or what it meant. Finally, when she felt she was under control, she sat down facing him across the table, and placed a hand on his. She knew there was no dissuading him. Once Father had made up his mind that was it, no argument. Oh, how alike they were.

For a moment they just looked at each other, father and daughter, too choked up to speak, knowing that by stopping his near-starvation diet and eating more normal food he was only bringing forward the inevitable. His days were numbered, and had been ever since he'd diagnosed the condition nearly three years ago. He'd been frank with his children then. They'd both known what the outcome would be, but now his statement had made it an imminent reality. Harriet got up and busied herself making the tea, trying to concentrate on that one act and blot out all else.

'Here you are, Father, nice and strong, just how you like it.' Their eyes met and they smiled at each other. It was a tragedy, thought Harriet, that it had taken his illness to bring them together.

'And I'll have a slice of toast and marmalade,' he said, glancing up at her with the old twinkle in his eye.

The letterbox rattled in the hall but Harriet ignored it and continued to spread the toast with a thin layer of butter and marmalade. She knew he had heard it too and felt the same dread tinged with eagerness, yet they had nothing to fear from the post, had they? Bad news always came by telegram.

She passed the plate of toast to her father and went out into the hall, trying to act normally, trying not to think as if, childlike, not thinking about it would make it disappear and turn this whole unbearable situation into a bad dream. Her father would not be dying but would be smilingly showing a patient into the surgery, and Alex would be waving as he left for the hospital.

Harriet shook herself, trying to clear the heaviness in her chest, the nausea, the panic, which threatened to overwhelm her. There was one letter on the mat and it wasn't from Alex, it was from Aunt Molly, judging by the handwriting. She would have to be told, and Alex of course, and everyone. Alex could put in for compassionate leave.

She took a deep breath and clutched the newel post for support. Everything felt unreal. They'd known for three years, she, more than anyone had watched their father fade away in front of her, yet now, only now, was it really happening.

'Anything from Alex?' he called, unnecessarily, as he did each morning. Their life had become so repetitive, but all that was about to change.

Harriet tried to regain her composure and speak normally. 'No, only one from Aunt Molly,' she called.

'Humph!'

She smiled despite herself at his reaction as she went back into the kitchen. His plate was empty and he was grinning up at her.

'I really enjoyed that!' And in the same breath he said, 'You'd better write to Alex today. They'll give him leave. I don't know how long I've got.' He said it almost cheerfully as if it was a relief to have made a decision. She longed to fling her arms round him as she had done when she was a child, but something held her back. A lot had happened between them since then, that was difficult to ignore.

'Read me Molly's letter,' he said, 'and then I'll be ready for another cup of tea.'

Aunt Molly was a large, busy-body of a woman, brusque, efficient and interfering, though well-meaning. After their mother's death she had come and helped raise the two children and keep house. When that was done and Alex was away at boarding school and Harriet was helping her father with his practice, she'd retreated, unceremoniously, back to her beloved Great Yarmouth. Sea air was a panacea for all ills, she declared, and she'd had quite enough of this London smog.

They'd been grateful to her of course, they couldn't have had a better surrogate mother for all her old-fashioned ways and fussiness. But after she'd gone the house had seemed to heave a great sigh of relief and settled back into a relaxed calmness, until, that is, two catastrophes occurred almost simultaneously. Their father's illness and the Great War.

'She's going to fuss,' her father was saying, breaking into her thoughts. 'She's going to fuss when she hears of my decision.' Harriet smiled weakly. How could he talk about it as if it was something trivial, like deciding to buy a new car? She watched him, fondly. His eyes were actually sparkling; he hadn't looked so alive for months.

'She will. She'll say it's the air to blame.' They both laughed and he caught her hand.

'Don't be sad, Harriet. It's God's will and who are we to question it? I'm not afraid. I'm just thankful I lived to see you and Alex grow to adulthood and I'm proud of you both.'

She tried to hold back the tears again but they overwhelmed her and it was a relief to cry. He pulled her gently down to kneel at his feet and they embraced each other while she wept, and in a strange way she savoured the moment and the feel of his thin arms tightly round her and knew she would remember it always.

'Good girl,' he said, stroking her hair as he had done when she was a child. 'You'll feel better now.' He lifted her chin so that their faces were close. 'I love you,' he whispered. She nodded and smiled and then took out her handkerchief and wiped her face.

'How about that other cup of tea,' he said, 'and then perhaps you'd better write to Alex and then to Molly. The sooner they know, the better.'

The sheet of paper in front of her on the desk had

remained blank for a full twenty minutes and the pen, hovering above it indecisively, had dried. She dipped the nib in the ink again and began.

Dear Alex. I hope you are well.

I hope you are well. What an inane remark! I hope this finds you well. How on earth do you start and finish a letter to someone in the thick of fighting? The middle was no problem, it was the beginning and the end. I hope you are well. Take care. It wasn't a bloody holiday! He was there in the midst of all that suffering and death, under constant fire, and had been for the best part of four years. What did you say to someone in that situation? Where were the words to say how you felt? Maybe they did exist somewhere, but she didn't have them. This letter, of all the many she'd written to him, had to be the best she could do. It was by far the hardest letter she'd ever had to write.

Usually, once the hurdle of starting was over, the words flowed from her hand until it ached, filling the pages with momentous happenings of Zeppelin raids over London, and, more recently bombing from aeroplanes, along with everyday trivia and family gossip.

This time the letter would be short. Nothing could precede or follow what she had to say to her brother. She took out a fresh sheet.

Dear Alex,

Father has asked me to write and let you know of a decision he has made. Since your last leave he has lost a lot of weight and hardly has the strength to walk any more. His very restrictive diet is robbing him of one of the very few pleasures left to him, and he has decided to abandon it. Is it possible for you to put in for immediate compassionate leave? I'm sure the authorities will be understanding. Having made his decision, Father seems relieved, even cheerful. I wish you could have seen how much he enjoyed a piece of toast and marmalade for his breakfast this morning! Please come home soon, Alex.

Yours with much love,

Harriet.

It was done. She read it through and wished once again that she had a better command of the language. It looked so trivial and simple, like a holiday postcard. There must be some more profound way of saying it, some way of pouring out her feelings and folding it up in the paper so that when Alex read it, he understood it . . . but of course he'd know how she felt! She put down the pen and turned the letter over to blot it, then folded it carefully and reached into a drawer for an envelope. She was going to need her brother so much.

The thought made her immediately feel guilty at her selfishness. Need him? How could she put that extra burden on him? *She* must be the strong one. He would need someone to lean on after what he'd been through, tending the sick and wounded constantly with only three short periods of leave in four years and now to be summonsed home to his father's deathbed. He had always been much closer to their father than she had. He'd been showing signs of strain in his recent letters too. A certain incoherence, a rambling, which was not like him at all. Alex was precise and exact. He wasted nothing, including words. It was just this preciseness, this coming to the point, this eloquence, which had given him the high marks he'd received in his exams in medical school. He always knew which were the salient points, what was important and their order of priority. He never dithered.

She took out another sheet and wrote a similar brief note to Aunt Molly. There'd be plenty of time for explanations and arguments. Aunt Molly would no doubt board the very next train after receiving the letter and the silent house would ring with her rather strident voice attempting to dissuade her brother from his decision.

Harriet got up from the desk, took off her apron and straightened her skirt. Stop thinking!

There was work to do and letters to post.

The door to the parlour was ajar and she looked in as she struggled into her coat.

'I've written to Alex and Aunt Molly, Father, I'm just going out to post them.'

He was sitting in his favourite armchair reading the newspaper. 'Take Ben with you. I don't think I can manage the gardens today.'

At the mention of his name, the black Labrador looked up and his tail thumped.

'Come on then, Ben.'

He needed no second bidding and sprung to his feet with an agility that belied his age. Harriet fetched his lead off the coat stand in the hall and clipped it to his collar.

'I'll give him a run in the gardens on my way back,' she said, clamping a hat on her head and giving herself a cursory look in the long mirror as she passed. 'Won't be long.'

The sun felt quite warm and she pulled the brim of her hat further over her face. Ben walked obediently by her side to the post office where she tied him to a post while she went inside. There were notices about the penny post being abolished. Harriet sighed. Everything was going up in leaps and bounds, some things had doubled since before the war. Now the Chancellor had raised taxes too, to pay for the incredible cost of this war, she supposed, but where was the money to come from?

Certainly many people were much better off than before the war, industry boomed, but for them personally, it was a struggle to keep on that big house now that her father wasn't able to practise. They only had his savings and what Alex sent home from his army pay.

She bought her stamps and looked at the letters for a moment before depositing them into the post box. Hurry home, Alex. Then she was outside again and Ben was wagging his tail, glad to see her, and she smiled. He could always cheer her up.

The gardens in the middle of the square provided a small area of greenery for local people to walk and sit, and for nannies to wheel their charges and gossip. It was not large but the oak and chestnut trees provided pleasant shade in summer. Now the trees were in full leaf but somehow the whole place looked rather drab and untidy and uncared for. Before the war the local council sent men to tend it periodically but with the lack of manpower in the last four years it had been thoroughly neglected.

Ben, however, was blissfully ignorant of this and as soon as his lead was undone, he ran off to sniff around the shrubbery while Harriet sat down on a wooden bench and gazed across the street at their house. She wondered what her father would think of the idea she'd had to bring his bed downstairs into the surgery. There would be room on the right by the window where he could enjoy the sunshine when he became too ill to get up. She sighed deeply and tried to get rid of the lump in her throat. He must hang on for Alex.

A black taxi blotted out her vision as it stopped outside their door and it took a moment before she realised who it was. Then she was up and running to the railings.

'Gwen!'

The young woman who climbed out of the driving seat spun round. Her small, pretty face lit up in a smile. She was wearing what looked like men's trousers and jacket and no hat. Harriet gasped.

'What have you done to your hair?' The cloud of unruly red hair, forever falling out of its pins, was gone, and in its place a mass of short curls clung to the well-shaped head.

Gwen giggled. 'Harriet, it's wonderful! So light and easy to manage. You know I always hated my hair, it wasn't meant to be long, so I had it cut!'

Harriet stared in disbelief. Short hair – and cut close to her head like that! She was speechless, reaching up to feel the knot of her own thick brown hair and securing a loose pin. How strange it must be.

'And if you're going to comment on my attire, I'm fed up with long skirts getting in the way when I'm climbing in and out of this taxi. Freedom for women!' She shook her fist in the air in a good-natured way. 'Are you coming for your lesson? I've got an hour before I have to report for duty.'

'Not today, Gwen.'

Gwen's face clouded over. 'What's the matter?'

'Oh, it's not Alex.' She had read Gwen's thoughts. 'It's Father.'

'I'm sorry. Is he worse?' She was genuinely concerned and Harriet's heart went out to her friend for her generosity, considering the fact that she and Father had had several very heated arguments and that he blamed her entirely for Harriet's interest in the Women's Movement. If he could see her now! And if he knew she was giving Harriet driving lessons!

Ben came up and began to bark and wag his tail at Gwen through the railings. It didn't seem right to discuss her father in the street like this but she couldn't ask Gwen in, or didn't want to today, of all days.

Nor were they unobserved. She could see a figure watching from the window of the house next door to theirs. Their neighbour, Henry Carpian, invalided out of the war.

She pretended she hadn't seen him and turned her attention back to Gwen. 'He's stopping his diet.'

Gwen had no medical knowledge but had gleaned enough over her four-year friendship with Harriet, to know what this meant without having to have it spelt out to her. Her face sagged in dismay and she reached forward and took Harriet's hand.

'It's not helping him much now,' went on Harriet. 'I've just sent a letter to Alex. I just hope it doesn't take forever to get there.'

The two young women stood silently for a moment, sharing their emotions, and then Harriet clipped Ben to his lead and walked to the gate. For once she wished that Gwen would get in her taxi and go before Father saw her. He neither understood nor upheld emancipation of women, though, despite what had amounted to a constant battle between them, she knew that he respected women greatly, it was just that he believed they had an important place in the world but not an equal one.

They had got as far as the door of the taxi and Gwen had her hand on the handle when the front door opened. Harriet's heart sank. Her father hobbled out onto the porch.

'Oh, hello Doctor Baker,' said Gwen, coming round the front of the car, hand outstretched. 'How are you?' She was direct as ever, with no sign of the awkwardness many people would have felt, having just been told of his decision.

Harriet held her breath as she watched him look her over, from her cropped hair to her trousers. Then, surprisingly, the corners of his mouth turned up with the hint of a smile and his eyes twinkled. He made no comment about her appearance, but said, 'Not too bad, thank you, Gwen. Just off to start your shift, are you?' He eyed the taxi with a wistfulness that brought a lump to Harriet's throat. His beloved Morris Oxford sat dormant in the rented garage like a hibernating animal awaiting the springtime of peace and the availability of petrol. For a long time after giving up his practice and daily rounds of patient visits, he'd still started up the motor from time to time, or given its gleaming paintwork a token polish, but that had ceased now too. Father may be old-fashioned in many ways, Harriet thought, but he had accepted the internal combustion engine with enthusiasm, especially when Mr Morris had started producing his British-made car in Oxford in 1912. It had certainly provoked much admiration from his patients.

Gwen nodded in answer to his question and walked back round to the driver's side.

'The way things are going, I may not have it for much longer. Petrol's so scarce now it's putting the fares up and people are preferring to go by hansom again. Next time you see me, you'd better have a carrot ready for the horse!' She laughed, but Harriet couldn't tell if she was joking or not about driving a hansom cab. She wouldn't put it past Gwen to try her hand at anything.

'Goodbye.' Gwen waved cheerily as she took out the crank handle, inserted it into its hole at the front and gave a couple of sharp turns. The engine spluttered into life and, with a smile of triumph at Doctor Baker, which was not lost on him, Harriet was sure, she climbed in and puttered away down the road.

'Humph!' he said for the second time that morning. 'Before long it'll be difficult to tell men from women if they go on like this.'

Harriet said nothing but followed him inside with Ben. She didn't want to incite any arguments today, although his statement had sounded more resigned than provocative. He and Gwen were tolerating each other with good grace and she was glad. Unlike that evening when they'd met four years ago.

She hadn't meant to get caught up in the suffragette demonstration that day, not that she didn't support them in a passive sort of way, but at the age of sixteen she didn't quite feel it affected her, and in five years anything could happen. As far as voting was concerned, she knew nothing of politics and was happy to let the men get on with it for the moment. Other things concerned her more, such as equal opportunities for women to follow the profession of their choice. That affected her personally. She wasn't satisfied just being general assistant and housekeeper to her father but had been biding her time until she came of age and then she would decide what road to pursue. Finding a husband and having children had never been her ambition, and who, quite honestly, would want to marry a tall, plain girl like her? To have been tall and elegant would have been something, but her figure was shapeless and on the heavy side, without a single redeeming feature. Her father never gave up hope though, introducing her to every eligible patient; it was a wonder they ever returned!

The day of the demonstration was imprinted indelibly on her memory. She'd happened to be passing Buckingham Palace and, it being a pleasantly warm May day, she'd decided to walk instead of going by motor bus.

The area in front of the palace was a mass of people and it was immediately obvious as to the cause for the demonstration by the banners being waved defiantly, and the shouts of 'Women have a right to speak!' and 'Let the King see the petition!

As Harriet watched from the sidelines there was a sudden surge forward and some women managed to break through the dense cordon of hundreds of police, waving Indian clubs and shouting. Then there was mayhem as a tide of blue poured out and police grappled with the leaders, toppling many of them to the ground in an undignified struggle. Harriet caught a brief glimpse of a familiar face, looking frail and ill as she was bundled into a police wagon. It was Mrs Emmeline Pankhurst, in her mid-fifties now, too old to be involved in this struggle.

Harriet felt nausea and an almost uncontrollable anger rising together in her throat as she watched the scene of abject brutality, here in England in front of the Royal Palace itself. It was unbelievable! She wondered if the King was watching and what he thought. She'd read about rallies and demonstrations but it was quite a different thing to witness one.

Suddenly, from the crowd emerged a woman, her red hair loose and resembling that of a clown, sticking out where it had been pulled from its pins. Her face was streaked with blood and her dress torn off the shoulder.

'Help me!' she gasped. 'I shouldn't be here. Cat and Mouse!'

Harriet sprung forward and quickly taking off her coat, flung it round the other's shoulders.

'Here. Put my hat on too!' She unpinned her hat and clamped it onto the woman's head, endeavouring to tuck the unruly hair under it. 'Have you got a handkerchief? Your face is bleeding!'

They hurried away from the scene but not so quickly as to arouse suspicion.

As soon as they were safely in Grosvenor Place they stopped for a moment so that Harriet could try to clean up the woman's face a little. People were giving them funny looks and there were always those who would be only too ready to inform the police.

'Thank you so much!' said the woman, regaining her breath. 'I couldn't bear prison again. You've no idea how we are treated, especially when we're on strike.'

Harriet had heard of the hunger strikes and the infamous Cat and Mouse Act the government had passed the previous year. As soon as the hunger strikes were thought to be endangering your health they gave you a temporary discharge with conditions, knowing that before long either you would have to return to complete your sentence or hopefully, you would be arrested again in the meantime.

'Come home with me,' suggested Harriet.

'I don't live too far away and my father is a physician. He can check you over and I'll put something on your face, it's still bleeding.'

The woman seemed to hesitate briefly but then smiled, lighting up her small face.

'You're very kind, thank you. My father would be furious if he saw that I'd defied the court order again. My name's Gwen, by the way, Gwen Hill.'

'Harriet Baker,' said Harriet. 'Here, just hold your handkerchief there, there's a motor bus coming. You're in no condition to walk.'

Their reception at home had not quite been as Harriet expected. Her father was openly hostile to Gwen, wanting nothing to do with any treatment for her. He had stared stonily at her and then his mouth had turned down in an expression of disgust.

'I'm sure you can see to this woman's injuries, Harriet, and then she can be on her way home.' He had turned and walked out of the surgery leaving his daughter staring after him, both embarrassed and incredulous at his rudeness, something she had never before seen. He'd always been the epitome of patience and tact, even with those of his patients who were inclined to be onerous and pushed him to the limits.

Gwen had tried to laugh it off. 'I'm used to that reaction,' she said with a shrug. 'They think we ask for all we get and that it's unladylike behaviour.'

'But Father's not like that. I mean, he doesn't usually allow prejudice to affect his relationship with his patients.'

'Don't worry, Harriet. I'm grateful to you, and as he says, if you could just clean up my wounds I'll be on my way.'

But it had not ended like that. It had been the start of both a close friendship between the two women and of Harriet's commitment to the Women's Movement, in spite of her father's strong opposition. No, that was an understatement, his outright fury at her involvement and constant condemnation of 'that woman' who was influencing her.

Only the war had brought some sort of reconciliation between them as the suffragettes turned their energies to helping in the war effort, and then her father's illness when he had needed her more. Latterly, he had mellowed too, and probably she had as well. It was a time for harmony, understanding and love.

two

The shrill whistle made Alex duck down before he'd even had time to think. His reflexes were good, sharp, weren't they? Keep your head down, was the perpetual cry. Keep your head down until you had to go over the top. Another close one, that. Who had bought it that time? When would his number come up? That's what they all said. You were all right if your number wasn't on it. He'd seen what happened when your number came up. Hundreds of them, thousands. The ones who were still breathing he'd helped to patch up and send down the line to the casualty clearing station and that was the last he saw or heard of them.

He could feel his body shaking but could

do nothing about it, and he was clutching onto something so hard that his fingers hurt. Waiting for the next one. There was always a next one. When would this bloody war end? Bloody! Bloody! Bloody! He heard a whimpering sound and then realised it must be himself. Someone sniggered. What was there to laugh at? He looked up angrily. A cluster of faces was looking at him through a haze of smoke and he became aware of the rhythmic jolt and sway of the train. One of the faces was grinning.

'What's so funny?' Alex growled.

The face grinned wider until it was wiped off with a whack from someone else's fist.

A voice snarled. 'You won't be laughing when it's you, sonny! You wait till you've been under fire for as many months as this poor bugger probably has.'

Someone gripped Alex's arm then and the voice was gentle.

'You're all right, chum, you're in a train heading for London. A spot of leave I imagine, like all of us. A good rest and you'll be yourself again in no time.'

The triteness of the words was lost on Alex and genuinely calmed him, or maybe it was the friendly, easy voice. He saw the three concerned soldiers sit back into their seats again.

'Have a smoke.' An open packet of Woodbines

was offered and Alex took one with shaking fingers. What was the matter with him? Was he cracking up? He'd seen it happen to so many. He tried to control the shaking enough to light the cigarette but a hand came out to steady his.

'Thanks.' He inhaled deeply and blew out the smoke. That was better. 'What was the noise?' He looked up as he spoke, to the owner of the hand, a large, beefy man with dark wavy hair and a moustache.

'The train whistle.'

'Stupid of me, I'm sorry. I must have been miles away.'

The big man nodded. 'It's difficult to leave it all behind, isn't it? Another world out there.' He eyed the white cross on Alex's sleeve. 'Medical Corps, are you?'

Alex nodded and the man fell silent. It was getting dark outside and raining and he watched the drops scudding down the glass. There'd been a lot of rain in France. And mud. Deep sticky mud. Men and horses had been devoured by it. He'd seen it happen and been unable to do anything. Orders were to keep going, look ahead. No time to try and rescue anyone. He'd lived through the experience in nightmares. Cold, sludgy mud, feet searching wildly for solid ground, down, down, dragged by a heavy pack, unable to breathe . . .

He shook himself and gazed at the raindrops

again, trying to concentrate through them on the darkening countryside speeding past. Trees in full leaf, unlike the stumps which was all that was left of those in the war zone. Here were crops flourishing and cows grazing and so much green. It was a different world all right.

There was a sharp pain in his right hand and he shook it involuntarily.

The still-smouldering cigarette stub flew into the air and landed on the floor between the seats where it sat, glowing until a foot reached out and ground it into the floor. The young soldier sniggered again and Alex was aware of all eyes on him as he sucked his burnt finger to ease the pain.

He opened his mouth to apologise again but changed his mind. It was humiliating how his mind kept wandering – and frightening too. He didn't seem to be in control of it at all. He must watch it or he'd end up off his rocker like some he'd seen.

Father. He should be thinking of Father. That was the reason for this leave, not for a rest like these others here. Ten days' leave he had. Compassionate leave to say farewell to his father, that is if he wasn't already too late. He was due back in France on the thirty-first.

It would be good to see Harriet too. It was almost nine months since he'd been home on leave, and then only for a week. And good old Ben. He pictured the dog leaping excitedly forward when he saw him and tears pricked his eyes. He was really going soft!

They were coming into the suburbs now although there was nothing to see in the darkness, especially from the lighted train compartment. Now and again the darker, angular shapes of houses loomed up, or a chink of light showed, but it looked dead, uninhabited in the black-out.

As the train slowed to cross the river and enter Victoria Station, the beefy man leaned forward.

'Are you all right, chum? Far to go, have you?'

Alex smiled, feeling more in control of himself now. 'I'm fine thanks. No, just a short ride home to South Kensington. I'll get a motor bus or cab.'

'If you're lucky!' the man replied, standing up and reaching to lift his kit down from the luggage rack. 'Ain't many of them around these days, according to the missus.'

The train jolted to a sudden stop, almost throwing the man off his feet. 'Gawd!' he spluttered, 'they got women driving trains now too? Wouldn't surprise me none!'

They shuddered forward again and then stopped once more, the locomotive letting out a sigh of steam as if settling down for a long wait.

'Now what's up?' Alex opened his window and looked out. All along the train others were doing the same. At first the banter was good-humoured but as the minutes passed it turned to a grumble. Precious leave was ticking away.

Alex felt pressure on his shoulders as someone leaned out above him. 'Oi! What's the hold up?'

Faces turned back from the compartment in front. 'Bomb on the line. Unexploded. They had a visit from Fritz this afternoon.'

'Just our bleedin' luck!' said the voice above Alex, and withdrew. It was the young soldier. 'Well, I ain't volunteering to move it!'

The big man was leaning out of the window of the door and he turned his head to look back inside. 'Nobody's moving nothing until it's defused, yer chump. Pity the poor sod that's got that job.'

Alex looked at the soldier, caught his eye, and tried to give an encouraging smile. He, himself couldn't be more than two or three years older than this lad but you grew up fast in a war. The boy scowled back at him, unappreciatively. 'It's all right if you know what you're doing,' said one of the others from the far corner. 'I'd rather be defusin 'em than be at the receiving end.'

'Yeah, yeah,' said the big man, heaving his bulk back into the carriage and sitting down. 'Nothin' to see out there. Might as well take the weight off my feet. We might have to walk from 'ere.'

Not even the young soldier, Alex noticed, was game to make any countering quip, but he himself could feel a bubble of laughter rising inside his belly but he quelled it before it erupted. He wasn't even sure what was funny. There was a bomb on the line, for heaven's sake! Why didn't the train move back further? They might all be in danger of being blown to smithereens any second. Where exactly was this bomb? Maybe it was actually under the train and that's why they weren't moving! Any shock or vibration might detonate it! Yes, that was it! That explained it. They were still half on the bridge too. Train and bridge would go up together! They were trapped! God! He must get out of here!

'Hey! What are you doing, chum? You can't get out here! Not until they tell us, anyhow.'

Alex felt a restraining hand on his arm and realised he had been about to open the carriage door. He hadn't been aware of standing up and reaching for the handle at all.

'I was just going to have a look,' he lied, looking into the face of the big man and reading his sympathy.

'We'd best stay put until we're given the word,' said the man, quietly.

Alex nodded. 'They must evacuate us,

surely?'

He'd no sooner said it than they heard shouts from outside and Alex leaned out again.

A guard was walking alongside rapping on every compartment door.

'Everybody out! We're evacuating the train. Please wait to be directed and you'll be escorted to Victoria Station. It's only a short distance.'

Alex was the first out. He lifted down his pack, opened the door and jumped down onto the loose rocks at the side of the track. It had become suffocating inside the compartment despite the open windows and cool, rain-spattered air. Now he momentarily lifted his face to the night sky and let the rain wash away his panic.

They waited in silence, watching as servicemen and a few civilians poured out of the train and stood obediently in the drizzle, waiting for the order to move. When it came, the long crocodile moved off. As soon as they were clear of the bridge they were directed off to the right in a wide arc, presumably to keep well clear of the bomb. Nevertheless, it was only half a mile or so before the gaping entrance to the station loomed up and Alex turned his thoughts to Father and Harriet again, the latter whom had promised to meet him here.

As they climbed the slope onto the platform, his heart thudded with excited anticipation. It would be good to see them again.

The crocodile of passengers was quickly swallowed up into the arms of the waiting throng.

Alex realised he had not said cheerio to his fellow companions as he scanned the crowd for Harriet's tall figure. He felt excited, and it was the first good feeling he'd had for a long time. Despite the reason for his home-coming he couldn't help but feel an elation, a bursting love within him.

It was she who saw him first. He felt a hand on his arm and turned to look into her handsome smiling face. There were lines of strain around the dark blue eyes but otherwise he saw no change in the clearly-defined cheek bones and jaw line of a face which she herself mistakenly considered plain.

Neither said a word as they opened their arms to each other and at the same time as feeling a surge of love for his sister, he felt fear in her rather too firm embrace.

'It is good to see you, Alex. You don't know how much Father is looking forward to seeing you too, he's very weak. I think he's just been hanging on for you.'

Her words struck him like a knife in his heart. Up to now it had seemed a little unreal but suddenly, as if a curtain had been pulled aside, he saw the truth. Their father was dying.

Again Harriet read his face. 'Gwen's waiting with her taxi,' she said as he shouldered his pack and they pushed their way through the crowd towards the exit.

He was shocked when he saw her boyish figure standing by her black cab, with her black trousers and jacket, cropped blaze of hair and no hat. He, more than anybody, admired women's efforts during this war. He'd seen plenty of proof of their ability and courage at the field dressing stations, which often came within firing range as the enemy advanced. He'd seen their dogged refusal to leave their patients when under fire, and he knew that here at home women were totally committed to the war effort. But this was going too far. Women, despite taking on more manly roles, should remain feminine.

She smiled warmly at him and held out her hand. 'Welcome home, Alex, even on such a sad occasion.'

It would be churlish to comment or indeed to treat her with anything but the normal respect one afforded a woman, so he shook her hand and gave her a small smile. He opened the cab door for Harriet and then stood awkwardly as Gwen hovered, waiting to see her passengers safely in. It wasn't right that a gentleman shouldn't open her door for her, yet she was the driver. What was the etiquette in this instance?

His moment of embarrassment was over in a second. She was ushering him in and closing the door after him, her clear blue eyes twinkling with amusement as she caught his look through the window. Then he watched with some discomfort as she cranked the motor into life, climbed in, and pulled out into the traffic of Buckingham Palace Road.

The very nature of women was changing much too quickly for his liking, not that he was any sort of expert. His experience of them had been limited to youthful flirtations during the odd concert visit or picnic party on the river in the limited leisure hours of first a medical student and then a doctor. Now those days seemed a lifetime away, a lifetime during which he had experienced more than his share of the horrors of war, yet he had never been in love. Talk often turned to sex in the rare moments of relaxation in the dugouts, and there was a lot of ribald bragging and teasing amongst the men, some of it harmless and some, to his unaccustomed ears, profane in the extreme. To be shocked or obviously offended in these instances only served to alienate him so he had learned to join in and to invent, as far as he could, a number of sexual liaisons, if only to be 'one of the lads'. He suspected that others did the same.

There had been one occasion, after all. He

chuckled at the memory of it. Quite a lark that had been, but also a milestone in his life, though he had admitted it to no-one, including the black-haired French tart with whom he'd spent the memorable ten minutes. She'd known it was his first time though, she must have, but he had to give her credit, she hadn't let on. Oh, he remembered that night all right. Always would. Four of them had gone together. They'd rung the doorbell and the woman who opened it had instantly seemed familiar in some way. It was only later that he realised she reminded him of Aunt Molly.

Alex giggled. Imagine what Aunt Molly would say if he told her! Aunt Molly, the epitome of correctness and decorum. The likeness had been in her manner, her fussiness, her chatter. The French Madam had babbled sixty to the dozen and none of them had understood a word. Maybe one day he would tell his aunt, just to see her reaction!

But slept with a woman? Not in the true sense of that pleasant euphemism, which suggested a whole leisurely night in the arms of someone you loved rather than a physical release paid by the minute. It meant cuddling up afterwards, warm and satisfied, and sleeping with her in your arms. He'd experienced sex but never made love and he wondered what it was like.

All this he thought as they chugged through

what he now recognised as Sloane Square. He stared at the silhouette of Gwen's curly head and now and again, by the dim light of passing traffic, was fascinated at the way her hair curled at the nape of her neck as she expertly, he had to admit, handled the vehicle through the largely horse-drawn traffic. The rain had stopped but in the near pitch blackness he admired the way she so obviously knew where she was going.

Harriet's hand was through his arm and she squeezed it fondly.

'You're miles away, Alex.'

He felt himself blush guiltily but knew she couldn't see in the dark.

'Are you all right?'

He knew what she meant but couldn't put it into words. How was he coping? What was it like? Oh, these people at home had no idea. No idea. God, they couldn't imagine . . .

'Yes, I'm fine.' He nodded and she squeezed his arm again. Better that they didn't know yet. They would know soon enough, when it was all over. Then perhaps, men would speak about it, or some would at any rate. Others would forever be unable to put into words the things they wanted to forget but never could. Many had already withdrawn into a private world from which they would never emerge. That was his worst fear. A living death. Better to be wounded in body than in mind.

Vivid images sprang up before him. Images of shattered bones bursting through flesh ripped open by vicious shrapnel, of walking skeletons ravaged by dysentery, of stinking suppurating gas gangrene. And the screaming . . . the screaming. Give the poor devil some morphia, for God's sake! He couldn't stand it any more! Stop the noise! Stop the bloody carnage! And then there was that final cruel act . . .

'Alex! We're home! Be calm! Be calm!'

He slowly became aware that the vehicle had stopped and he sensed rather than saw, two anxious faces watching him. He groped for Harriet's hand and gave it a squeeze.

'Home,' he repeated.

Gwen got out and came round to open the door. He stepped out onto the wet pavement and stood looking at the pillared porch of the house he'd always known as home, longing to step into its warm safe haven, yet dreading the moment with all his might.

three

'Thank you, Gwen,' Alex said, rather tersely, Harriet thought. He continued to look at her. 'You may be doing a man's job moderately well but surely there's no need to look like one too.' He turned away and climbed the few steps to the porch leaving Harriet to shrug at Gwen apologetically. Gwen, for once, was silent, standing in the glow of the headlights and looking stricken as though she'd received a physical blow. She turned briskly and got back into her cab, shut the door and drove away.

Alex was standing by the door waiting for Harriet to produce her key. This was not the Alex she knew. His face was expressionless and she bit back the sharp reproach she'd been going to make. There was no excuse for rudeness, yet she was worried about him. He hadn't said a single word all the way in the taxi and had obviously been miles away, first giggling to himself and then crying out.

She pushed the key into the lock and he followed her in, dumping his kit just inside the hall and removing his cap.

'Father's in the surgery now,' she said. 'We brought his bed down when he got too weak to climb the stairs.'

'We?'

'Aunt Molly's here. She's been a wonderful help.'

As if on cue, the surgery door opened and Aunt Molly swept through, removing her pince-nez and blinking at them.

'Alex! I thought I heard a motor car outside! I said to Alfred, "Here they are," a little late but then the trains are not as punctual as they used to be. War changes everything.' She opened her arms and gathered him into them as if he were a small boy, though he was at least six inches taller than her.

'Hello, Aunt Molly! It's good to see you!' His voice was quieter, Harriet thought, watching them affectionately. He was very subdued, even to the point of being withdrawn. He didn't return Aunt Molly's hug with nearly as much eagerness as he might, but was she reading things into it which weren't there? Of course he had changed. War couldn't fail to change people, and the transition from the battlefields of France to here at home in such a short time must be difficult. It would take him time to adapt as well as coping with the stress of their father's condition. She hoped they'd given him a generous leave.

Aunt Molly was leading him into the surgery and Harriet followed.

Their father was sitting up in bed by the window. He'd been asleep when Harriet had left but she was pleased to see that he was now quite awake and alert. A chair was placed by the bedside and there was a book upon it. Aunt Molly had obviously been reading to him.

'Hello laddie,' she heard her father greet his son with the old pet name and felt a twinge of jealousy which she guiltily shook off. That was the past, gone, surely she could forgive now? Be adult about it. Perhaps parents couldn't help favouring one child over another. She might know one day, in the unlikely event that she ever got married and had children. Now was now. She must just start from now, the present and the future. Never mind the past.

The difference in their father since Alex had last seen him must have been tremendous and Harriet could only try to imagine what Alex was feeling as he greeted his father. To her it had been a gradual thing, though these past few weeks, since he had stopped his diet, he had deteriorated dramatically. Every day as she bed-bathed him, he'd seemed to get thinner and it was incredible that he could still manage to get out of bed at all, albeit just to take the few steps to his armchair.

Aunt Molly babbled on cheerfully and Harriet blessed her, though she knew it was habit rather than tact. She could sense Alex's shock as he strode over to the bed and bent to kiss his father. Harriet could not hear the few murmured words which passed between them but both were smiling as Alex sat down in the chair and took his father's hand.

Harriet caught her aunt's eye and indicated the door. Leave them to each other, she thought, they had precious little time left together.

'I must go and put the kettle on,' said Aunt Molly, closing the door softly behind her. 'Alfred always likes tea at this time, but what about Alex? Do you think he would prefer cocoa? What do they have in the army?'

'Wait a minute,' said Harriet, catching her aunt's arm. 'Leave them together for a while. Tea can wait. You come and sit down, you've been on the go all day.'

Aunt Molly hesitated for a moment, an anxious look on her face. Then she smiled. 'All right, dear. I am rather tired. It's this bad London air. I always get breathless when I'm here. No wonder poor Alfred is so ill. I told him he should come and stay with me for a while and breathe some good sea air. I'm sure it would have done him the world of good.'

Harriet sighed, though good-naturedly. 'Father is diabetic, Aunt Molly. Not even sea air can do anything for that. He appreciated your invitation but wished to spend his final days at home.'

Her aunt settled herself in their father's chair in the parlour, arranging the cushion comfortably at her back.

'I know you say that, dear, but how can you know? We must hope, Harriet, there's always hope.'

Harriet seated herself opposite but didn't reply. She and her aunt had had this conversation many times over the past couple of weeks and she had learnt that it was futile to try to get her to understand the nature of the condition.

'I'll make the tea in a moment. You just sit there. You've done enough for today and we appreciate it.' She looked at her aunt earnestly. 'But what do you think of Alex?'

'Alex?' Aunt Molly looked up sharply. 'Tired,' she said. 'Drawn, pale, poor boy. Heaven knows what they must be going through out there.'

'He's not himself. I'm really worried. His letters recently have been a little confused and during the drive from the station he just wasn't with us at all. He was giggling, then crying out as if his mind was still over there on the battlefield, which is understandable of course, but . . .'

'How long is his leave?'

'I don't know. I haven't asked him.'

'What he needs is a good rest. I'm sure the authorities would allow him extra time if he's not well.'

Harriet was not sure extended leave was so easy to obtain but it would be worth inquiring. Surely it did not make sense to have unfit medical orderlies taking care of the sick and wounded?

She nodded. 'I must have a good talk to him. The shock and worry about Father must be adding to it.'

'He's young,' said Aunt Molly, 'time will heal. We can just be thankful that he got home in time.'

Harriet rose from her chair. 'Tea,' she said, trying to put on a cheerful smile to cover her irritation. Sometimes Aunt Molly made her want to scream, with her glib little clichés. Did she really believe them or was she covering up emotions she just couldn't face? If only life were that simple! If only there was someone she could really talk to who would understand. Even Gwen never seemed to have the time these days. She called in often enough but never had the time to stop and really talk.

When the kettle was whistling, Harriet poured the bubbling water into the teapot and then laid two trays, each with two cups and saucers. She took her time, covering the teapot with a cosy to keep it warm, making the task last twice as long as it should. At last she carried one tray to the surgery, balanced it on her arm and opened the door.

Alex did not hear her enter. He was sitting beside the bed leaning forward with his elbows on the counterpane. Their father was no longer sitting up but had slipped down a little. His eyes were closed and as Harriet stepped forward she could see that his face was relaxed and peaceful.

She put the tray down on the bedside table and Alex jumped as she came into his vision. She put a hand on his shoulder and as he looked up into her face she could see that he was totally aware, as he had been when they'd first met at Victoria.

She smiled. 'He's so pleased to see you.'

He could only nod and she saw that his eyes glistened. There was absolute honesty between them, none of Aunt Molly's avoiding the issue. No euphemistic remarks about their father's condition. They both knew the truth and spoke the truth, as did their father. They knew they didn't have to speak in whispers or put on any show of false cheerfulness. He knew the facts too and was ready to face them, always had been.

Now a smile spread across the face on the pillow and, without opening his eyes, he said: 'I certainly am.'

Harriet and Alex both laughed.

'I've brought you both some tea, Father.'

He opened his eyes now. 'What about you and Molly?'

'We'll have ours in the kitchen. I know you'd like to have Alex to yourself for a while.'

'And Molly does have a habit of dominating the conversation,' he whispered. Harriet smiled at his accurate reading of her motives. 'Just give us twenty minutes,' he said, 'Alex must be longing for a peaceful night in a comfortable bed.'

Alfred Baker had the best night's sleep he had had for a long time. When Harriet entered his room the following morning she found him cheerful and well rested. The jug of water on his bedside table was only half empty and the urinal beneath the bed had only been used once.

Alex too looked well rested, though his eyes lacked lustre and he just quietly smiled a greeting to everyone as they gathered in their father's room to breakfast with him, since they had no wheelchair to transport him to the kitchen. Alex could have carried him, of course, but it hadn't seemed worth it just for breakfast. Perhaps at dinner time.

Their father, surprisingly, did most of the talking, which was something, considering that Aunt Molly was present. Harriet watched as he chewed through his toast with an energy she hadn't seen for weeks, as if he couldn't swallow it quickly enough in his eagerness to talk. He never once mentioned the war, she noticed, as if having himself fought in the South African war he shared an unspoken understanding with his son. Can we truly imagine what it's like out there, she thought, or do only those who have been, know? Surely it would be better to talk about it, to expel the horrors, than to keep them cooped up inside your head? But what did she know?

'I'd like to see the car once more,' her father was saying. 'Take me out to see it, Alex. Start it up, let me hear it.' His eyes were alive and he wriggled in his chair and clenched his white bony fingers round the blanket on his knees as if it were the steering wheel and he was driving it now.

'Look after her well, Alex, and she'll serve you reliably for many a year.' He rested his head against the back of the chair, suddenly tired and Harriet stood up and started collecting the breakfast things onto the tray.

'Later then, Father. Have a sleep first, then I'll bring a bowl for your wash and we'll take you out to see the car.'

It was another pleasantly warm day and the front of the house was in full sun but Harriet insisted that their father was wrapped up well for his excursion. He hadn't an ounce of fat on his bones to keep him warm.

They carried his armchair outside first and placed it in the porch and then Alex lifted his father from the bed as deftly as he would have a small child and took him along the hall and through the front door. When he was suitably tucked up Harriet and Aunt Molly perched on the porch wall while Alex walked round the corner to the mews where the car was kept in a small rented garage.

They said very little while they waited, except to comment on the pleasant warmth of the sun and the mess the gardens in the little square were in. Again she glimpsed their neighbour watching through the bay window and felt irritated that they couldn't at least enjoy this moment of privacy. Did he have nothing better to do than spy on others?

She immediately felt ashamed. Perhaps that was all he could do. She had no idea how his wounds had affected him. They knew very little about him. He had moved in just before the war and lived alone. Then, when he was away fighting he'd employed someone to come in now and again to keep an eye on the house. He'd had a live-in nurse for a while but could now apparently cope on his own.

As the minutes ticked by Harriet cursed herself for not waiting until Alex had brought the car round before bringing her father out, but then she knew he wanted to hear it and see it appear round the corner. What was keeping Alex? Couldn't he get it started? It hadn't occurred to her to wonder if he even knew how to drive. He hadn't done so before the war.

'She might be a bit difficult to start,' said her father as if reading her thoughts. Harriet longed to go and see if she could help. Gwen had taught her a trick or two . . . but of course she couldn't! Even if she dared let her father know, she couldn't humiliate Alex. She'd seen what he thought about women having anything to do with cars.

Aunt Molly shifted her position irritably. 'Sitting on this cold brickwork is going to give me rheumatism. I do wish he would hurry up, though why we're all sitting out here anyway, I can't imagine. Noisy, smelly things!'

'Then either fetch yourself a chair or go inside,' said her brother, sharply, taking Harriet by surprise, and her aunt too, judging by the dumbstruck look on her face. She said nothing but remained where she was.

'And they are neither noisy nor smelly,' went on Alfred, enjoying himself. 'The sound is pleasant to the ear and as for being smelly, horses are far worse. You remember as well as I do, Molly, on a hot day the stench of tons of manure in the streets was overpowering. Motor cars cause no such problems.'

Harriet smiled inwardly and avoided her aunt's face. She'd been put very firmly in her place. No-one dared say anything against motor cars in her father's presence!

The slow chug of an engine caught their attention and a gleaming chrome radiator and rounded black bonnet nosed into view and then made its way along the kerb coming to a standstill immediately in front of them.

Alex grinned out at them and waved in a silly fashion. He let the motor run for a few more minutes and then switched it off. The car gave a shudder and was silent. They all watched Alex step out and shut the door and Harriet said, 'It is attractive, I must say.' She reached out and took her father's hand, knowing what he was thinking. His eyes held an expression which was a mixture of both deep sadness and awe.

'Take me for a drive in her, Alex,' he said.

'But Alfred . . .!' began Aunt Molly. 'You'll

catch your . . .' she stopped. 'I don't think you're strong enough! It's madness!'

'Of course it is, my dear Molly.' He was showing signs of fatigue Harriet thought. The excitement, the fresh air and the sunshine must have contributed to it. 'But don't interfere! It won't be the first mad thing I've done in my life but it will probably be the last.'

Harriet watched the indignant, worried expression on her aunt's face change to one of sad resignation and knew that at last she seemed to be facing the truth about her brother's condition. As Alex went and opened the passenger door of the car and then came back to carry his father to it, she put an arm round her aunt's shoulders.

'Come on, Aunt Molly, there isn't room for us all. We'll go and put the kettle on and have a hot cup of tea waiting for them when they get back.'

She couldn't help but stay a moment to watch Alex as he engaged the starting handle and turned it two or three times before giving it a sharp pull up. Nothing. The next time it fired, then died and she suffered his embarrassment for him, knowing what their father would be saying if he were well. As it was, he was looking agitated and she sensed, too, his frustration at not being able to jump out and help his son. She blinked back the tears which sprang to her eyes and then smiled through them as, at the third try, the motor caught and settled to a rhythmic throb and Alex dashed back to adjust the hand throttle. With a crunch of gears and one or two jolts they moved forward.

'Look at that!' said Aunt Molly at her side. 'All that palaver! Give me a horse and trap any day!'

'You can't stop progress,' said Harriet as they went inside. 'And it has given Father a lot of pleasure. I remember when he first bought it new in 1912, he was so proud of it! He often used to do house calls to patients when they were quite able to come to the surgery, just for an excuse to drive it.'

'Humph!' was all her aunt said as they went into the kitchen.

'While you make the tea I'll air the surgery a bit and change the bed linen,' Harriet said. She caught her aunt's look. 'Don't worry! I'll only open the window for a few minutes.'

The room was heavy with the overpowering, sweet rotting apple smell common to the breath of all diabetics in the late stages of their illness and Harriet lifted the sash and stood for a moment enjoying the fresh air in her face. She could hear the chink of crockery from the kitchen. Normal everyday sounds, yet this wasn't a normal day. Amidst August sunshine and people drinking tea there was sickness and death all around. There always was, she supposed, in the course of life, but far, far more in these last four years of this dreadful war. Just a short distance away, across the Channel, the big guns roared and men were dying in their hundreds of thousands to gain a few yards of muddy ground. In the newspapers they dressed it up in optimistic terms but you only had to look at the lists of casualties to know the truth. What was the personal message Sir Douglas Haig had delivered to all ranks last month? She closed the window and straightened the curtains, trying to remember the exact words.

'Every position must be held to the last man: there must be no retirement. With our backs to the wall and believing in the justice of our cause, each one of us must fight on to the end.' Sighing, she straightened the bedclothes and stood up. It was murder. Sheer, bloody murder.

The kettle had hardly boiled before they heard the chug of a motor car and the slight squeal as it was brought to a halt outside. Harriet went to open the front door and looked in surprise as Gwen climbed out of her taxi.

'I thought you were Alex,' she said.

Gwen raised her eyebrows.

'He's taken Father for a drive.'

'Oh.' She seemed a little disappointed. 'How is your father?'

'All the better for seeing Alex. Come in.

We've just made tea.'

Gwen glanced along the road. 'Perhaps it would be better not to.'

Harriet put a hand on her friend's arm. 'He's not himself, Gwen. Forgive him.' Why did it matter so much to Gwen what Alex thought about her? She didn't usually let other people's opinions worry her. Harriet looked at her friend shrewdly but said nothing.

'I know,' Gwen sighed. 'You said his letters didn't seem right, as if they'd been written by someone else. Has he said anything?'

'Not a word about the war, or anything else for that matter.'

'Some of them don't like to talk about it. I wish Father was the same sometimes. He seems to want to pour it all out when he's home on leave and sometimes you can hardly bear to listen.'

Harriet nodded. She'd heard some of his experiences related by Gwen. It didn't do for those back home to be in ignorance. People should know what was going on.

'I came to tell you,' said Gwen as they made their way to the kitchen, 'that I'm out of a job so no more driving lessons for you. It's too expensive to run motor cabs now and I've no experience with a horse so . . .' She shrugged her shoulders.

Aunt Molly beamed at Gwen over her pince-nez but Harriet noticed the smile fade as her eyes focused on the short hair and then travelled down, taking in her attire.

'Fashions are changing so rapidly nowadays,' she said, 'especially here in London. My, if you were to walk in the streets of Great Yarmouth dressed like that . . .' She left the sentence unfinished.

Gwen laughed. 'This isn't fashion Miss Baker, it's practical. I'm a taxi driver – or was until today. They're going back to hansom cabs to save petrol.'

'Ha!' said Aunt Molly with satisfaction. 'What did I say?'

'It's only temporary.' Harriet smiled. 'While there's a shortage. Once this war's over cars will be really popular, you'll see.'

'Well, sit down, my dear.' Aunt Molly changed the subject. 'Harriet will get out another cup and saucer.' She lifted the watch on a chain hanging round her neck from the depths of her bosom and peered at it. 'It's really time they were back. They've been gone twenty minutes. Do you think that wretched machine has broken down?'

'Of course not. Don't worry, they'll be here soon.' Harriet turned to Gwen. 'What will you do now, then? Knit socks?'

Gwen giggled. 'Pity any poor soldier who received any socks I knitted. I haven't thought about it yet. Maybe ambulance driving.'

'What, over there? But Gwen, you couldn't cope with looking after wounded men, you know you couldn't.'

'Thanks for the vote of confidence.'

'You know what I mean.'

Gwen shrugged and there was no time for further discussion as they heard a car door slam and Harriet rushed to the front door to hold it open. This time it *was* them. Alex already had their father in his arms.

'Go straight through to the surgery and I'll bring the tea through, Alex.'

Their father looked drained, exhausted, hardly able to hold his cup. They'd all taken their tea into his room, Gwen too. He'd greeted her with a slight smile, Alex's greeting had been merely a nod. Now she stood up.

'All the best, Doctor Baker.' She bent over the bed and grasped his hand and he smiled properly, though tiredly. She looked round. 'Goodbye Alex, Miss Baker. I'll see myself out, Harriet.' And she was gone and they were silent until the front door closed. Before Aunt Molly could stir up any criticism about her friend, and whose opinions, she knew, would be held by all except herself, she gathered the tea things as she had done earlier that morning.

'Let's leave you to rest, Father, unless you want Alex to stay?'

'A little later,' he whispered. 'Come and see me later, will you?' He turned and raised his eyes to his son who had risen and nodded before following the two women into the parlour where he slumped down into an armchair. Aunt Molly seated herself on the sofa and reached for her knitting bag and Harriet took a chair next to Alex.

'We haven't had time to talk,' she said.

He smiled and shook his head, avoiding her eyes.

'How long is your leave?'

'Ten days. I've got to take the train back on the thirtieth.'

Aunt Molly looked up sharply. 'Only ten days! Oh, but I'm sure they'd let you have longer if you explain the situation.'

Alex looked at her with mild exasperation. 'They do know the situation, Aunt Molly. That's why they gave me leave and they certainly won't extend it. Some poor b . . . some poor blighters out there haven't had any leave in eighteen months or more.'

'What if you were . . . not quite fit to go back?' asked Harriet, tentatively.

'So long as I can hold a rifle I'm fit in their opinion. Why, don't you think I am?' He was frowning and looking at her accusingly.

'Well, I just thought you were exhausted.

Wouldn't you do your job better if you were more rested?'

He relaxed back into the chair. 'If they sent every man home who was exhausted they'd have nobody left.'

She left it at that. Alex gradually closed his eyes and, as much as Harriet would have liked to talk to him, she realised he needed rest more than conversation. His gentle breathing plus the click of Aunt Molly's knitting needles was restful and Harriet found her own eyes closing too. She mustn't nap for long, there was dinner to think about. She'd managed to get a nice piece of haddock.

It was the clock chiming twelve which woke her up with a jump. Heavens! She had really dozed off. Alex was still asleep and even Aunt Molly's knitting had fallen to her lap and she lay back with her mouth open, her pince-nez at a crazy angle on her nose.

Harriet got to her feet. She must have slept for a good forty minutes! How disgraceful, in the middle of the day! Trying not to disturb the others she crept quietly out, closing the door behind her. She would just look in and see if Father was awake. Frequent short naps seemed to suit him best.

He looked peaceful, the skin of his thin face smooth and flaccid over the bones, but Harriet

felt a tinge of alarm and went closer to the bed.
The sweet acetone smell was particularly strong.

'Father?' She stared hard at the bedclothes
over his chest. Were they moving imperceptibly?
With trembling hands she turned back the covers
and reached for his wrist. There was a faint but
rapid pulse. He took several deep breaths as
though he couldn't get enough air and then was
quiet again.

'Alex!'

He was there in a moment, by her side.

'I can't rouse him, Alex! He's in a coma, isn't
he?' Their eyes met.

'There's nothing I can do, Harriet,' he
whispered, and then flung himself down on
his knees beside the bed, grasping his father's
shoulders and sobbing into the bedclothes. 'Not a
bloody thing I can do! He's dying and I can't help
him!'

She knelt down beside him, her arm round his
shoulders as he sobbed. 'We're here with him,'
she said, 'that's the main thing now.'

A cry at the door reminded them of poor
Aunt Molly, and Harriet wordlessly got to her
feet and led her aunt round to sit in the chair
next to her brother's bed. Then she resumed her
place next to Alex, whose sobs were quietening a
little, her fingers on her father's pulse. She felt it
gradually become feebler and at last it stopped.

She remained calm and dry-eyed, knowing that her tears would come later. Alex looked up at her, alarmed, and read it in her face.

He let out a cry then, a long, despairing, heart-wrenching sound and his eyes held a wild madness in them that struck Harriet with a terrible fear. He leaned forward and grasped his father's body in his arms, crying into the shoulder that was now still and could comfort him no more.

'Alex.' Harriet gently pulled him away. 'I'll call Doctor Morris. He can come to Father and also give you a sedative.' Come to sign the death certificate, was what she meant but she couldn't voice the words just yet. She looked across at Aunt Molly who had remained silent all along. She was sitting like stone, staring at the body of her brother, unblinking.

'Aunt Molly,' Harriet held out her other hand to her but she shook her head without looking up.

Alex allowed her to lead him like a small child up the stairs to his room. He was quiet now, his face expressionless, eyes blank, as she led him to his bed. He lay down on it and turned to face the wall, curling up, childlike, and she covered him with a blanket from the other bed. Then she bent to kiss him as if he were her child, and left the room.

four

The hands of the clock had seemed to stand still as they waited for the hearse to arrive at the appointed ten-thirty. Even Aunt Molly, who could usually be relied upon to fill empty time with often trivial chatter, had fallen silent.

Harriet had positioned herself where she could observe Alex. During the week since their father's death his behaviour had varied enormously, sometimes almost his old self again but often, like this morning, distant, withdrawn, hardly seeming to know where he was and unable to carry out even the simplest routine actions without prompting. She had even had to oversee his dressing, select the dark suit from his wardrobe hoping it would still fit, borrow a black tie, ironically from their father's wardrobe, and hang it round his neck, where his fingers had performed the well-practised act of tying it. Even then she'd had to straighten it for him. Alex had withdrawn inside himself. Now he sat in what had been their father's armchair by the hearth, feet together, hands in his lap, tense, unnatural, like someone waiting to be summonsed to an important interview.

The clock struck the half hour and as the chime died away there was a knock at the front door.

Aunt Molly stood up and felt her hat to make sure it was still in place. Harriet rose too and went over to Alex. He turned his head to look at her and she could see that he was with them again. He nodded, got up and put on his hat. Harriet took a deep breath and walked to the front door. The sooner this painful part was over, the better for all of them, especially Alex. He had barely two more days' leave.

Flowers completely covered the coffin in a brilliant colourful blanket and spilled over onto the floor of the hearse like a display at a flower show. One of the black horses snuffled and scraped a hoof on the road, causing his plumed headdress to quiver and the driver murmured some calming words and tightened the rein.

She felt Alex take her arm and she looked up,

meeting his eyes. They were solemn but alive and she relaxed a little as she climbed into the funeral car.

The August sunshine lit the church with swirling dusty beams of light, bringing out the vivid colours of the stained glass and striking the silver eagle lectern with flashes which darted about like a spotlight as the vicar turned the pages of the Bible during his reading.

Harriet glanced round discreetly, recognising some of the faces in the large congregation as previous patients of her father's. They hadn't forgotten him, then. Pride surged up in her as she thought of this popular man who had been her father. A man who had never made a fortune in his career because he was not a business man but a doctor first and foremost. A caring, compassionate doctor who had seen patients as troubled people needing his skills, not as a means to earn a living.

He'd always had plenty of time to listen to his patients, why had he rarely had time to listen to her too? He had never even tried to understand her point of view regarding women's rights and had done nothing but criticise her, the way she dressed and behaved, even her choice of friends. She remembered, too, his embarrassing attempt to marry her off – or perhaps that had been more Aunt Molly's doing than his, for he would have lost his assistant. Her engagement had been short-lived and she was thankful she'd had the strength to call it off despite the disgrace. If marriage was not a priority in her life, a loveless one certainly was not.

Her father's patience with others had not seemed to extend to his family. Perhaps it was always the way with people in his profession. Perhaps you could only give so much of yourself and it was the families who suffered when you were drained. Aunt Molly had put up with his short temper and his dictatorial manner with acceptance. Her generation of women had been like that.

Alex . . . Alex had always been their father's ally, justifying his shortcomings and acting as mediator, but never the target of his wrath, that had been reserved for the women.

Harriet felt a little guilty at her thoughts as the congregation stood for the final hymn and Alex moved forward and joined the other pall bearers to carry the coffin on its final short journey.

The small group clustered round the grave, heads bowed, dark and sombre in the midst of the fresh green grass and luxuriant summer foliage. An occasional soft breeze caught the vicar's cassock and it fluttered gently making him look like a great white bird amidst a flock of ravens.

'. . . and we commit the body of our brother,

Alfred, to the ground . . .'

Harriet was aware of the chirping of birds and the gentle rustle of the leaves as the vicar intoned his prayers. She could smell the newly dug earth and she stared at the hole into which her father's body would shortly be lowered. She wished she'd known him better, tried to understand his point of view. If only they could have discussed things more.

The thick black of her long dress absorbed the warm sunshine and she could feel the intense heat of it burning her back and a trickle of perspiration begin to run down from the nape of her neck. Her head felt a little light and she shuffled her feet to change her position. Please be over soon, she thought.

The vicar stopped talking and closed his prayer book and the coffin was gently lowered into the ground. Alex's arm was against hers and she felt it shudder. He was crying softly. One by one they grasped a handful of soil and threw it onto the coffin and then the crowd began to move away. Alex was still crying softly and she put an arm around his waist and held him to her. Aunt Molly, on the other side of him, clasped her hand and they remained there for a long time until Harriet thought she was going to faint in the heat. She lifted the veil from her hat and mopped her forehead with a handkerchief and then reached up and gently wiped Alex's tears.

It was Gwen who urged them gently away, taking Harriet's other arm and steering them along the path towards the waiting car. She caught a glimpse of Henry Carpian's face in the crowd. Their eyes met briefly and he gave a slight nod.

The two women climbed in with Alex between them and Gwen stood outside watching their departure. She'd bowed to convention on this occasion, Harriet thought, looking at her friend with affection. She wore a long black skirt and wide-brimmed black hat probably borrowed from her mother, and it all but hid her face which looked pale by contrast. The only sign of her usual flamboyant self were the curls of bright hair framing her face like tongues of a flame.

Harriet leaned against the front door after the final guest had departed and hesitated to turn round and face the quiet emptiness of the house and her life, which, for the first time, was like an empty book waiting for her to write in it. Suddenly and frighteningly, she had the freedom she'd always wanted and now she wasn't sure that she did want it. It had been easier when she had known her role, her day-to-day routine, first helping her father in his work, then, latterly, nursing him. She missed him already, despite their differences. Even when he'd been lying ill and semi-conscious she'd felt his presence. Now it was gone.

'Are you all right, dear?' Aunt Molly came out of the surgery carrying a tray laden with left-overs. The surgery would always be the surgery, wouldn't it? Waiting for the war to end and Alex to start up in general practice.

She nodded in response to her aunt's inquiry. 'Let me help you.' Her voice echoed in the emptiness. 'Where's Alex?'

Aunt Molly shrugged slightly. 'Probably lying down, poor boy. It's all been such a shock to him, he was so close to his father.'

Harriet nodded again. If she hadn't known her aunt better, she'd have resented the implication that she herself had not been close to him, but Aunt Molly was not capable of such reproach.

'I'll just go up and see.'

She knocked gently on his door. There was no reply.

'Alex? May I come in?' Still no response so she opened the door and went in.

The room was empty and the bed made. Nothing seemed out of place, it was just as they'd left it this morning before the funeral, dressing gown neatly draped over a chair. But something was different. His dark suit was hung up on the wardrobe door and the black tie placed neatly on the bed. So he'd been up here and got changed, but where was he?

'He's not there. Are you sure he's not in the

parlour?' Despite her aunt's denial, she went to look herself. 'Alex?' she called. He was nowhere in the house.

'Gone out for a walk,' suggested Aunt Molly, tying an apron round her waist. 'Wants to be alone for a while.'

Harriet felt apprehensive. Alex had changed but her aunt couldn't seem to see it. Not just mourning his father, it was far more than that.

'But he didn't tell us.'

'Come on, dear, let's get the washing up done. He'll be home soon, no doubt. After all, he's a grown man. He doesn't have to account for his movements.'

'But it's the normal thing to say when you're going out,' flared Harriet, following her aunt into the kitchen. Things weren't normal though, were they? They were in the midst of this dreadful war and poor Alex, along with thousands of others, was facing God-knew-what. Of course he wanted to be alone. 'He must have left while people were still here,' she said, picking up a tea towel and starting to dry the china.

By late afternoon Alex was still not home and Aunt Molly's temporary calmness had been replaced by her usual fluster.

'I hope he hasn't been run over by one of those dreadful motor cars,' she said, 'and it's getting cooler now, he'll catch a chill, especially in this bad city air.'

Motor car! Harriet sprang to her feet and rushed out into the hall calling over her shoulder: 'I won't be a moment!' She grabbed her coat and flung open the front door and went down the steps to the street. Motor car! Had he taken the Morris? She reached the garage in the mews and wrestled with the big wooden doors. They creaked open to reveal an empty space. The car was gone. He *had* taken it! But where had he gone? She racked her brains to think of somewhere or someone who could give him comfort at this time. Or maybe he was just driving. She wondered if he knew that he wouldn't be able to buy any petrol. There had been a full tank before he'd taken their father for a drive the other day, but that wouldn't get him far.

'He's taken the motor car,' Harriet told Aunt Molly who had come to meet her at the door and now stood wringing her hands and staring bleakly at her niece. She turned to stare at the telephone on the hall table.

'Do you think we should telephone the police?'

Harriet shook her head. 'As you said earlier, Aunt, he's a grown man.'

'Yes, but . . . the funeral . . .'

Harriet took her aunt's arm and led her into the parlour. 'We've just got to wait and pray,' she said.

Alex did not return that night or the next morning. Harriet herself was in two minds whether to contact the police. Aunt Molly would have done it herself had she not an inherent fear of things modern and not understood, like the telephone.

Neither woman had slept very much the previous night, listening for his knock at the door, or key in the lock – if he had his own key with him. Very little traffic had passed during those long hours, just the occasional omnibus rumbling by in the distance and the clop clop of one or two carriages. Harriet's eyes stung with lack of sleep as she stared at her aunt across the kitchen table, where neither of them could do more than sip cups of tea.

'He's due to go back to France tomorrow night. What are we going to do if he doesn't return?'

'Of course he'll be back by then, dear. Plenty of time.' Her aunt sounded over-confident as if trying to convince herself. 'We must telephone the police.'

'And if he isn't found in time?'

'Don't be silly, girl! If he isn't here, he can't go back, can he? They'll have to extend his leave. He's not fit to go anyway, until he's more rested.'

Harriet jumped up from the table. 'He has to go back! Don't you understand? This is wartime! It's the army, not school! We can't just send a note to excuse him! I'm going to see Gwen.'

Aunt Molly's reaction was to burst into tears and Harriet immediately felt contrite. She had never spoken to her aunt in this manner but sometimes her ignorance and naïvety were intolerable. The sight of her aunt crying for the first time since her father's death seemed to snap some emotional barrier deep within herself and suddenly pent-up grief exploded from her and they clung to each other, weeping for Father and brother Alfred, and for Alex and in some part, for themselves. Like a summer storm, it cleared the tense atmosphere and some moments later Harriet repeated her intention to ask the advice of her friend.

'I don't see how she can help.' Aunt Molly dabbed at her eyes and replaced her pince-nez.

'Because her father and her brother are in the army too,' Harriet persisted.

'Is one of them home on leave?'

'No, but they talk to her – at least her father does. He tells her about how things are. I'll speak to her and then we'll consider our next move. I shan't be long. I'll take Ben. The poor dog's been neglected and he's feeling the loss too.'

It was a good half hour's walk to Gwen's

house. She could have taken a cab, of course, or the omnibus, but it was better to get out of the house and the fresh air and exercise would do her and Ben good. The weather had held and was quite warm so that she arrived feeling rather hot and dishevelled. Gwen's mother opened the door.

'Hello, dear. Come on in. I'm so sorry to hear about your father. He was a good man and a popular doctor.'

Harriet stepped inside the small hallway. 'Thank you, Mrs Hill, that's very kind of you. Is Gwen at home, please?'

Mrs Hill rolled her eyes to the ceiling. 'Yes,' she said, 'she was laid off, as you know, and is moping around as if it's the end of the world. Gwen!' she shouted in the same breath, from the bottom of the stairs. 'Harriet is here!'

A door opened and Gwen appeared. She no longer wore her cabby's trousers but had on a lemon blouse and a rather short mid-calf length brown skirt. With her vivid hair she reminded Harriet of a tree in autumn.

'Come up,' invited Gwen. 'Bring Ben, he's all right.'

'Alex has disappeared,' said Harriet without preamble as they closed the bedroom door.

Gwen spun round, her face concerned. 'What do you mean, disappeared?'

'I mean he's taken the Morris and gone somewhere without a word.' She sat down heavily in a chair. 'He must have left while we were still entertaining people after the funeral yesterday.'

'You mean he's been gone all night?'

Harriet nodded.

Gwen was silent for a moment. 'But . . . you must have some idea. Friends maybe?'

'All his friends are away at war I imagine, and I never really knew any of them anyway, only one who was a great friend in medical school . . . I don't know where to start looking. Aunt Molly and I were going to telephone the police.'

Gwen shook her head vehemently. 'No! When does his leave end?'

'He's due back on Saturday. He's supposed to catch the late afternoon train to Dover on Friday.'

'Oh God!' Gwen looked stricken. The depth of feeling in her words made Harriet grasp her hand in an unspoken question.

'If he's not back, he'll be court-martialled for desertion.'

'Oh, surely not. We could report him as being ill, shocked by the war and his father's death . . .'

She knew she was beginning to sound like Aunt Molly.

'It won't make any difference,' said Gwen in a whisper. 'If he doesn't report back he'll be classed as a deserter.'

'And then what?' asked Harriet.

In a barely audible voice Gwen said: 'Deserters are shot.'

five

The hand on Alex's arm was solicitous, he knew that from somewhere deep inside, from his other self from the past, but the fingers seemed to burn through his sleeve and weld themselves to his skin so that he wanted to throw them off and scream at them to go away. This tiny part of himself still had some control, only just, and prevented any unconventional behaviour, so that outwardly he continued to play the part of grieving son and brave soldier in his expression and murmured appropriately at the stream of well-meaning tributes that washed over him.

He was leaning against the oak desk, his hands grasping its familiar edge while the room heaved and swayed a little like a balloon about to burst and even more faces appeared at the door. The air was heavy and stifling and the babble of voices and clink of china seemed magnified. The ex-patient of his father's gave a final comforting squeeze to his arm and moved away out into the tide.

Alex loosened his grip on the desk and his fingers encountered something cold and greasy. Looking down he saw that someone had put their plate of half-eaten sandwich on the desk and a piece of discarded ham fat was hanging over the edge onto the green leather inlay. Alex stared at it with disgust and a rage began to bubble up from somewhere inside him. How dare they come to pay their respects to his father and at the same time defile the very symbol of his work. This desk was sacred, an altar, why hadn't Harriet or Molly covered it over? They'd had no thought for his father like he had. Harriet and their father had never seen eye to eye, her and her ludicrous feminist ideas, and Molly? Oh, Molly cared in her own way. Her own simple way. She had no sentiment though.

He carefully replaced the piece of fat on the plate and looked round for somewhere else to put the whole nauseous lot. Next some wine would be spilt and the stain would be there forever like blood, a symbolic reminder perhaps, of both his father's profession and the state of the world.

As a further wave of mourners headed in his direction he picked up the plate and walked straight through them. His name was spoken but he ignored it and he headed for the kitchen to deposit the plate and its contents onto the draining board. He'd had enough. Enough. They would suffocate him. He had to get away.

There was a crash of breaking china from the other room and Alex's brain had conditioned him to fear and instantly react to any loud noises. His reflexes sent him diving under the table, banging his head as he did so. There he lay, curled up, knees up to his chest, waiting for the pain to subside before he made a move. That was a near one. Some poor bastards must have bought it. How many more friends must he see die? Blown to bloody pieces. He gave a sob and crawled out of his shelter. 'Jack?' he called softly. 'Eddy? Are you there, chums?' Bent double he ran stealthily out into the hall and up the stairs.

The place hadn't changed at all. The same gentle water flowed over the green-carpeted stones and gurgled through the clump of rocks which halted its progress and formed the ideal fishing hole. The same flat rock jutted out into the stream. His rock. Alex stepped out onto it and as he did so felt a lightening of his body, an almost euphoric sensation as if he'd just stepped out of a mad world into Paradise.

It was the same rock, solid as always. Grey and flat and cool. Reliable and immovable. He knelt down to examine the front edge and ran his fingers slowly along the grooves which he had carved there all those years ago. A.A.B. Alexander Alfred Baker. The grooves were lined with lichen so he clambered back to the bank and searched until he found a twig, then back on the rock he began scraping the grooves clean and washing them out with handfuls of water until his initials stood out as if he'd only just finished carving them.

'What are you doing there, laddie? You've been scraping away there for an hour.' He could hear his father's voice now. If he twisted and looked up he would see him too, bending over, smiling through his heavy moustache, his thick brown hair dishevelled and flopping over his forehead. He would have on that old green jersey he kept for fishing trips, and the plus fours, and bare feet for wading out into the stream.

He'd inspected the carving and grinned and ruffled Alex's hair. 'It's time to go. By the time we hitch up the pony and get home it'll be past six o'clock and I've got an evening surgery.'

Alex peeled off his shoes and socks and lowered his feet into the water, still sitting on the rock and flinching at the icy coldness. He rested his feet on the velvety algae-covered rocks and waggled his toes. The water was only about a foot deep just here. He wondered if anyone else knew about this place. No reason why they shouldn't, although it was some way from the road. He remembered once seeing someone on the opposite bank further downstream. He'd felt a sort of anger tinged with fear at their private place being invaded, but his father had waved and called out a greeting and was obviously unperturbed by the stranger's presence. Alex had refused to acknowledge the man, even look at him, and his father had been annoyed at his apparent rudeness. The day had been spoilt.

There was no-one here now, only the trees whispering in the breeze, and the birds who lived amongst them. The sounds were having a hypnotic effect on him and he felt his eyelids growing heavy. He couldn't remember the last time he'd had a good night's sleep.

'Why don't you go further up the bank and have a wee nap?'

Alex's eyes snapped open, his father's soft tones still ringing in his ears. Yes, he would do that. There was a grassy slope further up the bank behind him. He'd just rest for a while. He left his shoes and socks where they were and stepped across the scattered stones and on to the bank.

When he awoke, the warm afternoon had faded and cooled considerably, in fact it was almost dark. Alex sat up and looked around. It wasn't often he and his father stayed here overnight, in fact they had only done so twice before when he'd got a locum in to take the evening surgery and be on-call for the night.

But here they were again. He couldn't quite see his father in the gloom but he was here somewhere, he knew. What was that hump over there? That must be him. He'd turned in early. Alex didn't remember eating though, he was really hungry, but he knew where the bag of provisions was. He stood up unsteadily and picked his way gingerly in his bare feet towards the large oak where he knew there was food and a warm coat. There was a paper bag filled with sandwiches and two or three assorted cakes and a few apples. He bit hungrily into a ham sandwich. Better leave some for tomorrow or Father would be annoyed. He settled back to sleep.

The bright morning sunlight on his closed eyelids brought him slowly back to consciousness and he luxuriated in this gentle awakening, slowly stretching from the curled-up position of sleep and rolling onto his back, then kicking off the warm overcoat that had covered him. When he opened his eyes he saw the bright green of the foliage moving and swaying across a pale sky and he watched, mesmerised, with heightened perception and admiration and wished he could lie here forever. Gradually the soothing sounds crept into his cluttered brain, pushing out the memories of gunfire and explosions and the cries of dying men. Into their place came the chattering of a cluster of birds high above and the murmur of the stream.

Alex lifted himself to a sitting position and looked around. He couldn't see his father. He must have gone for a walk before breakfast. He'd soon be back and then they'd light a little fire and boil some water for tea. That's where he must be, collecting some firewood. Alex got to his feet wondering where he'd left his shoes and socks. Father would be bound to ask if he saw him in bare feet.

Look at his clothes! He brushed off the bits of grass and tried to smooth out the creases in his trousers then ambled down towards the river. There were his shoes and socks, on the flat rock. He didn't remember leaving them there. He lay full length on the rock and splashed his face with water making his skin tingle. It felt wonderful!

'There you are, laddie! About time too! Half the day is gone already and we've some more fishing to do!'

Alex smiled and continued to splash his face and run wet hands through his hair, then on impulse, he began to strip off all his clothes and when he was naked he stood up in the water and splashed himself all over, vigorously rubbing his skin. He laughed aloud at the ecstasy of it and splashed harder, swishing his feet back and forth, squealing with delight.

'Hey! You'll frighten the fish!' He pretended not to hear. At last he jumped up and ran up the bank to look for a towel but there was none in his bag. Strange they should have forgotten that. No matter. The sun would soon dry him. He felt suddenly invigorated and began doing some exercises in the little clearing. Stand, squat, stand, squat. Then some press-ups. Ten. Fifteen. Twenty. Now for breakfast. There were still some sandwiches in the bag. He ate two and an apple and then went and dressed again but left off his shoes and socks and rolled up his trouser legs. Now for some serious fishing.

'Good luck!' his father called from somewhere upstream. 'Catch something tasty for supper and Aunt Molly will be pleased.'

Bait on the hook, cast the line – and wait.

Oh, he could wait now. He could wait all day. He would never tire of fishing. Never, never, never. He felt refreshed and alive and happy.

Alex sat there on his rock, motionless, loose fists one above the other holding his imaginary rod, staring at the gentle water and smiling.

six

Harriet stared at Gwen hoping she had imagined those words *deserters are shot* . . . There was a hollow, nauseous feeling in her stomach and her legs felt too weak to hold her up. She heard her voice in the distance as if it belonged to someone else.

'We kill . . . our own men?' She sat down on a nearby chair as her legs gave way and she felt Gwen's comforting arm around her shoulders.

'I wouldn't lie to you Harriet. It may not happen in Alex's case, probably not, he's a doctor . . .'

But they were *all* good men suffering unimaginable fear and pain.

'How could they?'

'To set an example Father says, to deter others. What's more, the firing squad is made up of men from their own company who know them.'

'It's barbaric. It's murder.'

'I know. There'll be a scandal after the war. I'm sorry, I shouldn't have told you.'

'Yes, yes, I have to know what the stakes are.'

The stakes were high. Higher than she had ever imagined.

'There's time yet.' Gwen helped her to her feet. 'I'm here, Harriet. Any time.'

'Any news?' Harriet stepped into the hall and unclipped Ben's lead. She hung her hat on the peg, aware that her aunt had come to meet her and was standing silently behind her. When she didn't answer Harriet spun round. Molly's powdered face was streaked with tears and she held out a piece of paper.

'What is it? What's wrong? Alex . . . ?'

Aunt Molly still stood mutely and the hand which held the paper trembled. Harriet stared at it and recognised a piece of their own telephone message pad. She slowly reached for it, searching her aunt's face for clues of its content before she dared read it herself. This day was fast becoming one of major shocks.

It was not addressed to anyone in particular and scrawled in large child-like letters so unlike the old Alex. *Gone to find some peace. Don't worry. A.*

Harriet let out her held breath in a sigh of relief. 'But he's all right. He'll be back.' She looked up at her aunt. 'We never really thought of looking for a note, did we? What made you look in the telephone pad?'

'It rang,' Molly said in a tremulous voice. 'It rang and I picked it up. I thought it might be Alex.' Harriet nodded, knowing that in normal circumstances she would have ignored it. 'It was Mrs Drew.'

'Mrs Drew?' Harriet wished she would just get on with it. Who on earth was Mrs Drew?

'My neighbour in Great Yarmouth.'

'Oh, yes.'

Aunt Molly's face crumpled. 'My house has been hit by a bomb.'

Harriet felt again the guilt at her impatience as she flung her arms round her aunt's shoulders. 'Oh, no! Come and sit down and tell me about it.' She guided her into the parlour and sat her in an armchair, then seated herself opposite. 'What did Mrs Drew say exactly? Was it a direct hit?'

Aunt Molly took out her handkerchief and began dabbing at her eyes, shaking her head at the same time. 'No. My neighbour on the other side got it. Poor Mr Lambourn.' She couldn't speak for another moment and Harriet waited patiently, holding her hand.

'My house has slight damage on that side. Windows broken and a crack right down the wall.' She looked into Harriet's eyes. 'I'll have to go home, dear. You do understand, don't you? I hate to leave you alone and with the worry of Alex and everything. What did your friend say?'

'Oh, nothing much, and I shall be fine, don't worry. Alex will be back and feeling more able to face the war again and I shall . . .' She'd been going to say 'I shall find some war work to do' but thought better than give Aunt Molly more to worry about. 'I shall have enough to do here to keep me busy. Come on, I'll help you pack and then we'll find out the times of trains from King's Cross.'

It was just gone two o'clock when the cab dropped them off outside the station. Harriet had been going to ask the driver to wait but decided at the last minute to see her aunt off on the train properly and then get the omnibus back. They'd left a note for Alex if he should arrive in their absence. If he still wasn't back Harriet had some serious thinking to do – but that was later – for the moment her aunt needed her. What devastation she was going back to, heaven knew! Harriet could only hope it was relatively superficial.

The station was crowded with young men arriving from the north on their way to the front. The mood was jovial but probably bravado, Harriet thought. They had no choice, did they?

The train was in and they found an empty compartment. Harriet reached up and opened the door, climbed in and then hauled her aunt's bag up onto the luggage rack.

'Do let me know about Alex, dear.' Molly took off her coat and hung it on the hook and then plumped herself into the corner and opened the window. Harriet climbed back out onto the platform and shut the door.

'Of course I will. And of course I want to know about the house as soon as possible.' There was nothing more to say. They stared at each other in mute sympathy. The engine hissed loudly, doors slammed, the whistle blew and the train shuddered and clanked into motion. Harriet waved until it was out of sight and then stood, feeling suddenly very alone. She was going back to an empty house unless Alex was back. Please God he was! But he would be gone soon anyway and then she had to face loneliness and start making plans for the immediate future. Long term plans must wait until the war was over.

Oh, come on, stop feeling sorry for yourself! She straightened her hat, turned and marched briskly towards the exit. She might be living alone now but she certainly wasn't lonely, she had plenty of friends, hadn't she?

The omnibus was full and the talk was not of the war but of an impending police strike. They were asking for more pay and the Prime Minister, Mr Lloyd George, was negotiating with the unions. Another topic was the worry about the epidemic of Spanish influenza which had reached London in May and seemed to be spreading. Harriet half listened to the conversations round her on her short journey but her mind was mostly on Alex. She had remembered the name of his friend in medical school. It was Ken Winterton. Was there any point in telephoning Charing Cross hospital or was he away fighting the war too? She racked her brains to try and remember if Alex had mentioned him in his letters.

Alex was not at home. The house was quiet as she let herself in and Ben ambled into the hall, his tail wagging. Harriet glanced at the clock. Half past three. Alex would be in soon, surely. Today was Thursday. He still had twenty-four hours before departure. Plenty long enough. It wouldn't take him long to pack, then down to Victoria. On impulse she went up to his room. If she could find his papers she could check the train time. It seemed wrong going through his things but she had to know how long he had left.

It was in a side pocket of his kit bag. Seven o'clock train to Dover. He was being posted to another casualty clearing station of his battalion near Amiens and further away from the area of intense fighting where he'd been for so long. That was something. His mental instability had obviously been noticed.

But the next morning there was still no sign of him and she was glad when Gwen appeared on the doorstep.

'What should I do?' she asked for the umpteenth time, as if her friend could suddenly come up with the answer. 'He doesn't mean to desert, he's not well, he's exhausted, surely they would understand.'

Gwen was shaking her head vehemently. 'Nobody would accept that. How could you prove it? The way they understand it, if he doesn't return when he should, that constitutes desertion.'

'I can't believe what you said, Gwen, that deserters are shot. They wouldn't kill their own men! I've never heard anything like that! Isn't our justice system second to none?'

'Not in wartime. Do you think what we read in the papers is the truth? They tell us what they want us to know. Believe me, Harriet. Dad tells me the truth.'

'I'm not doubting your father, but it's unfair!' Harriet thumped her fist on the arm of the chair and then sprang to her feet. 'I can't believe they'd be so unfeeling. I've got to help him!'

'What's fair about war? I feel just as frustrated about it as you do.'

Something in her tone made Harriet look sharply at her friend and she caught an expression which took her by surprise. 'You're in love with him!'

Gwen nodded slowly and gazed back at Harriet bleakly. Her freckles were conspicuous against the pallor of her face. Then she said, in barely more than a whisper, 'It's not reciprocated. I don't think he even likes me, you know how he feels about women's rights.'

She must have been blind! Harriet had had no idea. Poor Gwen! 'I'm sure he likes you, Gwen, just give him time.' Harriet turned to look through the window. 'Things are changing for women and people will get used to it. At least some of us have the right to vote now. We're showing them we're capable and intelligent and . . .' A thought burst into her mind. A thought so monstrous that she was silent for a moment as it formed properly in her brain. She swung round. 'Gwen! I've had an idea! It may be crackpot but it's all we have.'

She saw her friend's face brighten. 'What?'

'I shall go in Alex's place!'

Gwen laughed, but without humour. 'Crackpot? It's insane!'

'But look at me! The last thing you'd call me is feminine. Flat-chested, shapeless figure. I'm almost as tall as Alex and he's going back to a different clearing station where no-one will know him. I've helped my father enough to know almost as much as he does about patching up wounds.'

Gwen was shaking her head. 'When have you patched up wounds? You know about surgery, even minor injuries, but these are terribly mutilated casualties. You will have to lift them and carry them on stretchers. God knows what you would be expected to do and however much you know, you are not a doctor.'

'You believe we're as capable as men.'

'As capable in many ways but not as strong physically. This is not the time to try to prove something.'

'Of course I'm not going just to prove something!' Harriet flashed. 'I'm going to save Alex's life! I'm not totally ignorant, Gwen. But don't forget, all soldiers are not Douglas Fairbanks. With conscription everyone has to go, even the weak and timid. They won't be expecting a woman so they won't see one. I may make a slightly effeminate man but I won't be alone. I have to do this Gwen, I have to!' She paced up and down feeling an excitement tinged with terror that she'd never known in her sheltered life. It was akin to the feeling she'd had at the suffragette's rally when she'd only just escaped arrest, only far, far greater.

Gwen was silent now, her small face pinched and her blue eyes glossy with tears. Harriet held out her arms and the two women embraced each other and released their pent-up fears and emotions in a long-overdue weep.

'You're not really serious about this are you, Harriet?' They sat at the kitchen table with a plate of cheese sandwiches and a pot of tea. 'It was a wonderful thought but how can you be in the close company of men day and night without being discovered? I mean, have you thought of latrines, showers, shaving, look at your chin, smooth as a baby's bottom!'

Harriet rubbed her chin involuntarily.

'You may succeed for a while but sooner or later you'll be discovered,' said Gwen. 'Then it would all have been for nothing.'

Harriet sank down into a chair, deflated. It had been an insane idea but for a moment she'd been carried away. Now she could see that what Gwen said was true. Who knew how long this war would last and how long could she hide her true identity from the men?

'I have to do something . . .'

'You mentioned a friend of Alex's?'

Harriet nodded. 'I remembered his name. Ken Winterton, but he's probably out there too.'

'No harm in telephoning.'

It took ten minutes for Dr Winterton to answer the telephone. He sounded breathless and weary.

'I'm sorry,' said Harriet, 'I know you are very busy. I'm Alex Baker's sister and I wondered if you had seen him?'

'Seen him? I thought he was in France.' The voice was brusque.

'He came home on leave. Our father died.' She heard him murmur condolences. 'Alex is . . . not well. I think it's what's called shell-shock. He took the car and has disappeared without telling us where he was going. I'm worried that in his present state he won't realise what day it is and he's due to leave for France tonight.'

There was a pause. 'I'm sorry, I haven't seen him, Miss Baker. He hasn't contacted me at all. In fact, I haven't heard from him for months.'

'Oh, well thank you,' said Harriet. She shook her head at Gwen as she put down the telephone.

'Alex seems to have lost touch with him.'

seven

It was the cold which woke him. The cold and the hunger. He never remembered feeling so hungry in his life. Alex struggled out of the coat which had covered him during the night and sat up, confused.

It was a grey morning and threatening rain. An unseasonal chill ruffled the leaves and rippled the surface of the water.

What in God's name was he doing here? It was the old fishing place by the river where he'd come many times with Father.

Father was dead. It came back to him like a punch in the belly and he sat back down and leaned against the oak. Father was dead. His funeral had been . . . yesterday? Was it yesterday or had he been here longer? How had he got here?

Vague impressions floated around in his mind like lost dreams. Sitting on the rock, paddling in the icy water. He pulled out his pocket watch but it had stopped. He supposed he hadn't wound it. God, Harriet would be worried and he had to be back in France on Saturday. That meant leaving on Friday night. Was today Thursday or Friday?

As he splashed river water onto his face his hand lingered on his stubbly chin and he stood upright, sharply, letting rivulets trickle down his neck while a sudden awful fear invaded his mind and threatened to tip the delicate balance once more.

The growth of beard on his face seemed considerably more than one would expect over one day or even two. He'd last shaved on Wednesday, before the funeral he presumed. That day was so hazy he couldn't remember doing it but surely he had. Harriet would have reminded him.

Alex rubbed his chin again. He'd never grown a beard or moustache, despite current trends, and people's hair, facial and otherwise, grew at a different rate. Nevertheless, it couldn't grow so much in one day. That meant it must be Friday! He had to move quickly.

The petrol gauge had been on empty for some time when he finally arrived at their garage in the mews and put the car away. Luck was on his side so far, he could have been stranded and had to walk home. He had no money in his pockets and must look like a tramp, crumpled and unshaven.

The door opened promptly after his knock and Gwen stood, staring at him, a mixture of emotions on her face which he could not interpret. She glanced furtively up and down the street.

'Come in. Quickly!'

'What are you doing here? Where's Harriet?'

A fear was starting again, deep in his belly, making his heart thump and his mouth go dry.

Gwen closed the door and turned to face him and he was surprised to see her eyes glistening with tears. She reached out her hand and grasped his arm.

He almost shook it off, fear turning to anger. 'Is Harriet here, and Molly? Speak to me, Gwen, for God's sake!'

'You've been away for three days, Alex.' It was all she said, a single sentence, but the power of it exploded inside his head like a mortar and the world seemed to stop.

'*Three* days?' he whispered and the sound shattered the silence.

She nodded.

'Oh my God!' He covered his face with his hands and his knees felt weak. He was aware of her leading him into the kitchen and pushing him onto a chair.

'It's Saturday,' she said, 'and you should have left for France last night.'

Alex tried to struggle to his feet. 'I must go now. Get my kit.'

Gwen's hand was firm on his shoulder. 'It's too late, Alex, and you're in no fit state . . .'

He looked up at her, stupidly. 'Too late?' Her red hair curled elfinlike round her small, serious face. 'Harriet nearly went in your place. I had a job to convince her not to.'

Gwen, standing in front of him, real and solid one minute became hazy, her voice echoing inside his head. He was aware of a strange noise issuing from his throat and his fists hurt as he pounded the wooden table. Tears ran down his cheeks and he felt as if his life was draining out of him. He was not a man. He was less than nothing. A cowardly creature who deserved only to skulk in the shadows like a gutter rat.

He was a deserter from his comrades at war and now a burden to his sister. A firing squad was too good for him. But it wouldn't come to that, would it? He wasn't a deserter, he was absent without leave. That wasn't the same, was it? If he went back now, he would be punished, but . . .

He could hear shouting and realised, somewhere deep inside that it was himself. It was as if he were outside his body watching someone else, who, in their rage, was tearing the kitchen apart. Somewhere a dog growled, then yelped.

When he emerged into reality again, Gwen was sitting next to him, holding his hand, and a steaming cup of tea was on the table in front of him. The kitchen looked as if it had been hit by shellfire, with broken crockery strewn on the floor and a cupboard tipped over.

Again he shook her hand away and reached out a shaking hand for the cup, scalding his mouth as he drank thirstily. Inside, he felt churned up and nauseous and he could feel his heart beating.

'You don't need to stay,' he said, roughly.

'I'm staying until Harriet gets back. She's gone shopping. You can't go out, people might ask awkward questions.'

'Go!' he snapped. 'I shan't be hiding like the coward that I am. Do you think I'm going to sit around here all safe and cosy while my sister risks being arrested for hiding me?'

'Alex! It won't help if you give yourself up. You know they don't accept that shell-shock is a medical condition . . .'

'To hell with shell-shock! I'm a bloody coward, that's all!'

Her voice remained calm. 'You know the authorities may court-martial you for being AWOL. They won't show any leniency . . .'

He half rose from the table. What did this interfering woman know? 'I don't want leniency,' he said through clenched teeth. 'I want what I deserve!'

Gwen faced him squarely, unafraid and angry now. 'You know how unpredictable they are. You might get a punishment or it could be worse, far worse. Are you willing to suffer that because of your guilty feelings? How will that help Harriet? She'll have lost the brother she is trying to save and what will happen to her? What is the penalty for harbouring a deserter?'

Alex could see that he was beaten for the moment. He felt too tired to continue arguing with this woman.

'The only way you can help Harriet now is to stay here and try and keep out of sight. I've told my parents that I'll be coming over here a lot to help Harriet as she's on her own. It's all we can do, Alex.'

Something occurred to him. 'Where's Aunt Molly?'

'She went home on Thursday. Her house had been damaged by a bomb.'

'Poor Aunt Molly.'

'Only superficial, I believe.'

'But she'll probably come back here.'

'We'll have to think of some way of getting round that and putting her off.'

'You don't know Aunt Molly.'

There was a kind of quiet acceptance between

them now and, for the moment, a truce. Although the weight of the problem had not lifted, Alex was aware of his extreme hunger again and he rose stiffly from the chair and walked to the larder.

'Sit down,' said Gwen, softly, 'and I'll make you some breakfast.'

He caught her eye and her face softened into the hint of a smile.

He ate heartily and afterwards felt physically better than he had done for a long time. Then he went and bathed and when he came down Harriet had arrived home and she and Gwen were clearing up the mess in the kitchen. Ben was again in his bed and his ears went back when he saw Alex.

Harriet flung her arms around his neck. 'Oh Alex, I was so worried for you. I'm so glad you're back.'

If only he had come back yesterday, he thought. Then all would be well. Incredible that one day can make the difference between being within the law and being outside it. He was now absent without leave and he knew only too well what the consequences could be. Only too well.

eight

She had to hide him. There was no question of him returning to France, not in the state he was in. Harriet did not know what penalty returning late would incur. What happened if you were AWOL and then you turned up? Court-martial? And what then? Was it as Gwen said? Firing squad. She shuddered. She didn't know and she certainly was not going to ask.

Following his return Alex had fluctuated between insisting on returning to France and sinking into a world of his own from which it was almost impossible to rouse him. If he decided to go back there was nothing she could do, she had to leave that to him, but the more time that elapsed, the more serious the problem would be.

He had picked at his food at supper time and then retired to bed early. In the morning they must make a plan. No doubt the authorities would be coming to investigate his absence and they should have a contingency plan, somewhere for him to hide. She hated the thought of flouting the law and knew that in his right mind, Alex would too. A part of her thought it would be best to confront the situation, make a clean breast of it and report to the authorities, then take the consequences. But what if Gwen was right? What if he would be court-martialled and sentenced to death? Could they take that risk? She could hardly believe the army would ever carry out that punishment.

They would have a talk tomorrow. If Alex was in a more normal state of mind they could discuss it rationally. He could tell her the truth of what would happen to him.

Harriet hardly seemed to have been asleep five minutes when she was awoken by Alex screaming. He'd had nightmares since he had been home but none quite like this. Pushing her arms into her dressing gown she rushed across the hall into his room.

Alex was curled up in a tight ball with the bedclothes clutched to his face, sobbing and talking at the same time, although she could not decipher the words. It broke her heart to see him there, a grown man reduced to a frightened child.

She sat on the bed and folded him in her arms. 'Shhh. You're all right Alex. Wake up now. You are having a nightmare. You're safe at home.'

He clasped her hands. 'Not me! Please don't make me do it, please not me.'

'Alex! Wake up.' She freed one hand and stroked his forehead. At last he opened his eyes and she could see recognition in them.

'Harriet. They made me ... they made me ...' As if realising what he was saying he stopped, took a deep breath and relaxed a little.

'What did they make you do?'

He shook his head vehemently, then said, 'I'm sorry I woke you. I'll be all right now. Go back to bed.'

'Are you sure?'

'Yes, go on.'

She stood up but in the same instant heard a noise downstairs. Probably Ben, but she would go down and see just the same. He was getting old and deaf.

She avoided lighting the gas mantle as a thin shaft of moonlight lit her way down the stairs. In the hall she paused and listened again. Ben was in the kitchen but small sounds were coming from the surgery. Drawers opening stealthily, items being moved on wooden surfaces. There was an intruder. As if she didn't have enough problems, someone was robbing them!

All Harriet's worries and stresses of the past week were suddenly channelled into one big rage and she flung open the door.

'Who's there?' she demanded.

He had opened the curtains to give himself enough light to search the room and now that her own eyes were accustomed to the gloom she could see a small figure standing by her father's desk.

'Don't move!' Harriet rummaged in her dressing gown pocket for the matches and lit the gas. Both of them blinked in the sudden brightness but the boy made no move to escape. She was surprised to see a smug expression on his face instead.

'It ain't no use callin' the coppers, 'cause there ain't none. They's on strike.' He was about twelve she judged, his voice not yet broken.

'What are you doing? Shouldn't you be at home in bed? Your mother will be worried.'

He laughed. 'It was me muvver what sent me,' he chortled. ' "Coppers are on strike tonight so go and get somefink back from the rich up the West End," she said to me. She's got four mouths to feed and me pa's away in the war.'

Harriet smiled. 'We aren't rich,' she said,' but

you're welcome to some food. You only had to knock on the door. You won't find it in here, or anything worth stealing.'

The boy looked around. 'What is this? Some kind of office?'

'It's a doctor's surgery.'

His eyes widened. 'Oh, I ain't never been in no doctor's surgery before. We can't afford doctors.' He looked past her and she turned to see Alex standing in the doorway. She gasped. What was he doing showing himself?

'What's going on?'

'Who are you?' demanded the boy. 'Are you the doctor?'

Alex nodded.

'Don't doctors have to go and fight then? That ain't fair.'

'Well yes . . .' began Alex.

'Conchy are you?' said the boy, nodding his head. 'None of 'em want to go and get killed but they 'as to. Coward I call it.'

Alex opened his mouth to speak again but Harriet glared at him. What was he doing? He wasn't thinking straight.

'So missus, even *if* there were any coppers to call, you wouldn't fetch 'em, would you? I could tell them about him, couldn't I?'

She wasn't quick enough, should have had an answer ready, but he was sharp. He read her expression and grinned. 'I reckon we're even. Now, how about that food?'

Harriet turned towards the kitchen. 'How did you get in?'

'Winder,' he said. 'This 'ot weather people 'ave their winders open and then forget to shut 'em properly.'

Harriet nodded as she put bread, butter and a pot of home-made jam into a paper bag along with some left-over ham and a tin of sardines. She held it out to him.

'What's your name?'

'Jack.'

'Well, Jack, you can come here twice a week, Tuesdays and Saturdays, and I'll give you some food. Understood?'

He understood only too well. The sly grin crept across his face again. 'Bribery is it? I keep my mouth shut and you gives me food.'

'Just you, understand. We don't want hordes of children begging at the door.'

Jack grabbed the bag and scampered out of the kitchen towards the surgery.

'You may leave through the front door,' called Harriet.

Jack turned and rolled his eyes. 'The front door,' he mimicked. 'I'm honoured.'

After he had gone she closed the surgery window firmly and made a mental note to check all the windows each evening. Alex had already gone back to bed as she climbed the stairs.

The first thing on Harriet's mind the next morning was where to hide Alex. That was a priority. Although today was Sunday, they had to be prepared at any time for that knock on the door and act like a well-practiced drill. It had to be somewhere quickly accessible, yet not obvious. The first place she thought of was the cellar but although it was full of many years' accumulated items, anyone hiding there would soon be found. She sat in the kitchen with her first cup of tea of the day, going over the whole house in her mind, room by room. This was no game of hide-and-seek like they had played as children.

She drained her cup and put it in the sink, and still no answers came to her. Ben lay in his bed. He had looked up as she entered but not got up. She bent to stroke him. 'What are we going to do, Ben?' she whispered. The dog thumped his tail in response.

A sudden sense of urgency made her go and wake Alex before beginning her usual daily chores or even opening the curtains.

He answered her knock and she went in.

'No more nightmares?'

He shook his head. 'Did I dream the burglary

110

or was it real?'

'It was real. You may not have been aware of the police strike. He took advantage of that. The strike is over now, they came to an agreement yesterday but I expect things had not got back to normal . . . Alex,' she must talk to him while he was himself, 'they'll come looking for you. We must try and find a good, safe hiding place.'

He nodded and she could see that he was mentally searching the house as she had done.

'What would happen if you were caught?'

Alex shrugged. 'Court-martial I expect.'

'And then?' She watched his face. He did not answer immediately. 'What happens to deserters, Alex?'

He flinched and then began to tremble and Harriet cursed herself for being too direct, but she wanted the truth, no evading the issue. She had to know what she was up against and if what Gwen had said was true.

'No!' He was shaking his head as he had done after the nightmare. 'No, I'm not a deserter. No intention . . . Not, not, not . . . a coward . . .'

'Of course you're not. It was accidental. You didn't intentionally overstay your leave. Alex, tell me. If you report now and explain, will it be all right? I have to know. Will they let you explain?'

Alex looked her in the eyes and his eyes were like cold steel. 'They wouldn't listen. They never listen. At whatever cost they have to deter others from doing the same. It's so bad out there, Harriet, so bloody ghastly that given half a chance the sane human reaction would be to run, as far from that hell as you can go.'

Harriet nodded, realising how little was reported in the newspapers, how far from the truth it was.

'You want to know what happens to deserters, my little sister? They are murdered. Shot by their own comrades.'

'And you would be classed as a deserter?' she whispered.

Alex shrugged. 'I don't know. AWOL, desertion. It's all the same in their eyes.'

'Then we must make some plans now.' Harriet got up from sitting on the bed and tried to focus on practicalities. She reached up and opened his curtains.

In the street below a police car had stopped and two policemen were getting out.

nine

'Oh my God, Alex. It's the police. Run and hide. Quickly!'

She hadn't expected them so soon. Hadn't really known who to expect. Alex stood staring at her, afraid and yet puzzled. She grasped his arm. 'You must hide. Please.'

There was a loud rap on the door. At once Alex sprang out of his daze but still he didn't run. Harriet tried to push him out of the door but he resisted her.

'I'm not running. I'm not a coward. I would never let my comrades down. I'll stand and face the enemy like any good soldier.'

She wasn't sure if he was reliving the battlefield or speaking of the authorities as the enemy.

The rap on the door was repeated, more insistently.

'Alex, please,' she begged. 'The police are here. You must hide.'

'From Father? Are we in trouble? Is it hide-and-seek?'

'Yes, yes. Go and hide in your best place so he won't find you.'

Alex shambled towards the door and Harriet quickly pulled up the bedclothes in a semblance of order, then glanced around the room. Where was his uniform and his kit bag? She flung open the wardrobe door and saw his bag. 'Here, take this with you.'

She rushed down the stairs and then took a deep breath before opening the door.

'Miss Baker?'

'Yes.' She tried to look worried rather than in a panic. 'What's happened? Not Alex . . . ?'

'Alex being Lieutenant Baker of the RAMC?'

'Yes, is he all right?'

'We have a warrant to search the premises, Miss. Lieutenant Baker did not report back for duty. We understand your father recently passed away?'

'Yes, that's right.' Harriet tried to keep her composure. It was the hardest thing she had ever had to do. 'But what do you mean? He returned to France when his leave was over last Friday.'

The spokesman of the two held her gaze and she did not look away. 'His railway ticket was never used, Miss, and he certainly never reported to his commanding officer. We have therefore been instructed by the military police to find him and deliver him to them for court-martial.'

Harriet did not have to act any longer. The fear she felt was quite justified and it would have been unnatural not to show it. She grasped at the door to steady herself, at the same time opening it for them to enter. The younger policeman gave her a look of disgust as he passed as if he branded her just as much a deserter as her brother.

His superior, however, was solicitous and put out an arm to steady her.

'Why don't you make us a cup of tea while we search, Miss?'

'He's not here. Why would he be here?' She should have said that earlier. Wouldn't it be normal to deny it straight away?

'Nevertheless, we have to search.'

Ben had come out of the kitchen and he stood in the doorway and growled, however, he didn't make any move towards the two men. They both glanced at him but obviously didn't judge him to be a threat.

Harriet could do nothing but make her way to the kitchen. Where was Alex? Had he understood what he must do? Had he found somewhere safe? How could anyone hide from police who were used to searching houses? They know all the places to look.

She wanted to follow them but it wouldn't look right. She must do as they asked and pretend that although worried about the whereabouts of her brother, she knew that he was definitely not in the house. She hated all this subterfuge and deception. The most she had ever done was to fail to tell her father when she attended a suffragette rally or that she was taking driving lessons with Gwen. Minor things. Even then she had never had to actually lie. It was not in her nature and she was not good at it.

She put the kettle on the stove and heard the policemen climbing up the stairs; they had already finished with the ground floor. Sitting at the kitchen table Harriet strained her ears for any sounds from above. Any moment she expected the sound of voices followed by three pairs of feet descending the stairs and a look of triumph from the younger policeman, certainly.

The floorboards creaked as one of them entered the bathroom above. Where could anyone hide in a bathroom?

The kettle began to boil so she turned off the gas and poured the boiling water into the teapot. She heard murmurs above and held her breath, still holding the kettle. Had they found him? He wouldn't make a fuss, she knew that. He wouldn't resist arrest.

These were the longest minutes she had ever had to endure. It was as if time had slowed down. She reached for the cups and saucers automatically and poured in the milk as if she were entertaining friends to afternoon tea. Her hands carried out normal, ordinary actions while her mind was in turmoil and her emotions seemed to be suspended in limbo.

It was Ben getting up and growling again which alerted her to the fact that there was the sound of feet descending the stairs. How many feet?

She watched, mesmerised as a hand grasped the newel post followed by a uniformed figure. Harriet could tell nothing by his profile. As if in slow motion, he turned his head towards her as he reached the floor level and swung round towards the kitchen. His expression was bland, professional, giving nothing away. He held his helmet in his hand. No handcuffs.

The second officer followed and looked straight at her. He was disappointed.

Harriet held in her jubilation, she wanted to shout for joy and laugh with relief. She felt as if she would burst with all the pent up anxiety now released. She turned to pour the tea, wondering what the next logical question to ask would be. She felt like saying 'What did I tell you? I said he wasn't here,' but that would be childish. How would she feel if Alex *had* gone missing between leaving home and arriving back in France? They would still keep looking and trying to trace his movements. They weren't out of the woods yet by any means.

Harriet handed a cup of tea to the senior policeman. 'Please find Alex,' she said. 'I can't think what has happened to him. He would certainly not fail to return on purpose, that's not like him at all.' Be careful, Harriet, don't chatter on and say too much. She'd been about to mention his mental instability but thought better of it just in time.

'Oh, we shall, Miss,' said the senior officer, sipping his tea. 'The penalty for desertion is severe.'

Now she wanted them out. Out of her house. There was always the chance that Alex would come out of hiding. His hold on reality was so fragile.

Ben was watching the two men with suspicion but now his ears pricked up and he looked beyond them into the hall, causing one of the men to follow his gaze. Harriet's relief was short-lived and she almost held her breath, then got up and began gathering the cups and saucers rather more noisily than was necessary to cover any sounds from above.

But Ben settled again and finally the policemen got up and made their way to the front door, replacing their helmets.

'Thank you for the tea, Miss Baker. We'll keep you informed.' She realised that the younger officer had not said a word throughout their stay, but his expressions had spoken volumes.

Harriet closed the door behind them and leaned against it, trembling. Had they believed her? She was not an experienced liar and they were trained in observing suspects or witnesses. Didn't people show give-away signs when they lied?

Ben crept up to her, wagging his tail, and she bent to stroke him and calm her nerves. They would be back, she was sure of it, hoping to catch her off-guard. She and Alex must be extra vigilant.

It would be best not to call out to Alex but to go up and find him, she thought. Halfway up the stairs the phone rang. Sighing, she went back into the hall and picked it up, lifting the earpiece to her ear.

'Hello?'

'I see they didn't find him,' said a voice. 'You obviously have him well hidden.'

Harriet gasped. 'Who is this?' It was a man's

voice, so it couldn't be Jack, but Jack was the only one who knew about Alex – except Gwen of course, and she wouldn't play such a trick.

'Did you really think you could hide a deserter? How naïve you are, Miss Baker. Send him back to face the consequences like a man.'

Before she could reply she heard a click as the caller hung up, but by now she had a good idea who it was. Henry Carpian, the window gazer from next door. In fact, probably half the street had seen the police car outside their door. Was he, at this moment, telephoning the police?

She almost ran up the stairs. 'Stay where you are, Alex! They might be back. Stay hidden!'

There was no reply and her curiosity got the better of her so she continued looking for him. He was not in any of the three bedrooms or the bathroom on the first floor and that only left the attic room, and that was empty . . . except . . . of course! There was their favourite hiding place as children. She hadn't thought about that or been up there for years.

The attic was reached by a steep flight of narrow wooden stairs with a door at the top. It creaked slightly as she opened it and the mustiness and dust threatened to make her sneeze. She supposed the police had been up here, it wasn't hard to find.

What *was* difficult to detect was the small

door in the wall panelling which led to a cramped space in the eaves, probably originally intended as a storage area. She pushed the panel and the door sprang open.

Alex lay curled up inside. His face was ghost white and his eyes wide and fixed.

'Alex?' whispered Harriet. She reached out and touched his shoulder and he flinched.

What should she do? If Henry Carpian *had* telephoned the police, she ought to leave Alex there for a while longer, despite longing to hold him in her arms. Even while she hesitated she heard a knock on the door from two flights down.

She put a finger to her lips as if he were a small child. 'Don't make a sound,' she whispered, not even sure if he understood. Then she made sure the door was properly closed with no tell-tale gaps.

The only window in the attic was a skylight, so until she opened the front door she had no way of telling who was there. Fully expecting the police again, and wondering if she could pull off the deception a second time, she opened the door.

One man stood there, upright as a soldier should, no visible sign of wounds.

'Mr Carpian,' said Harriet, trying to sound like a normal person greeting a normal neighbour.

'Miss Baker,' he replied, looking past her and up the stairs. 'May I come in?'

'Of course. Come into the surgery.' She led the way, trying to calm her thumping heart and keep her legs steady as she walked.

'The surgery. How appropriate.' His smile held a touch of irony.

'In what way?' Harriet busied herself removing her apron and smoothing down her black dress.

'Because I assume it's where your father kept his drugs, and that is my price.'

She couldn't pretend she didn't know what he meant but should she pretend? How long could she keep up the charade? He knew that Alex was here and his price for silence was her father's medicines.

'Morphia to be specific,' he went on. 'My doctor refuses to prescribe more and the pharmacies will no longer sell it to me. I've rather come to rely on it.'

'I heard you were wounded. Surely if you are still in pain . . .' she heard herself say, still playing the hostess role.

'The pain is in here.' He tapped his head. 'It's called anger and bitterness and there's no instant cure for that, but morphia is some sort of compensation. So, Miss Baker, you let me have your father's supply and I keep quiet about your lodger in the attic.'

How did he know? Or was he guessing?

He grinned. 'I'm right, aren't I? My house is the same as yours and if I wanted to hide that's where I'd go.'

Harriet wondered if Henry Carpian had once been a different person. Had the war warped him or just brought out the worst in him? Without a word she went to her father's desk and opening a drawer, took out a key. With it she opened a cabinet on the wall.

'You might just as well let me have it all now,' he said. 'And then I won't need to bother you for a while.'

'You'll need a syringe and needles.'

'I have those but a spare would be useful.'

As she handed him the syringe, needle and two boxes each containing six ampoules of morphia, he held out both hands to receive them, and let one hand linger over hers briefly.

'Please go now,' Harriet whispered. 'Leave us alone.'

For the second time that day she closed the door and leaned against it in relief but this time her legs would no longer hold her up and she sank to the floor, shaking with grief.

She was being blackmailed by two people already. How many more would there be before this nightmare was over?

ten

Ten days later Ben died.

Harriet knew there was something wrong as soon as she opened the kitchen door. Normally Ben would be behind it, wagging his tail, his claws tapping excitedly on the lino as he greeted her, hardly allowing her to open the door, although during the past few days his movements had seemed an effort.

Now she found him curled up in bed looking as though he was still asleep. She stood with her hand still on the door handle staring at the inert body and hoping to see his chest rise and fall, but there was nothing. Harriet felt tears prick her eyes and she reached in her apron pocket for a handkerchief. Then all at once the strain of the past few days caught up with her and she slumped down at the kitchen table and burst into tears.

When the front doorbell rang she gasped and hastily dabbed at her eyes. Alex was still asleep. If it was the police back again he would be found and there was nothing she could do about it. She considered pretending to be out and went into the surgery to peek through the curtains of the bay window.

It was Jack! She had forgotten it was Tuesday. He'd been twice the previous week as suggested.

'You're early,' she said as she opened the door, trying to smile.

He looked at her curiously and she realised that there were probably no clocks where he lived. They just got up at sunrise and went to bed when it got dark.

'What's up?' he asked, stepping inside. 'Your brother been arrested?'

Harriet shook her head. 'Our old dog has died. I just came downstairs and found him.'

A look of concern clouded his eyes. 'Where is he?'

He followed her into the kitchen and stared at Ben. Then he slowly crept forward, knelt down beside the dog's bed, and reached a tentative hand out to touch him.

'I reckon 'e's not been dead long, 'e's still warm.' He gently stroked Ben's head. 'I 'ad a dog friend once,' he said. 'He wasn't mine but we was friends for a while. Then I never saw 'im again.'

'We've had Ben for fourteen years,' said Harriet, 'since he was a puppy. He was one of the family. We shall miss him a lot.'

'I could get you another dog,' said Jack, turning to look earnestly into her face. 'There's plenty where I live.'

A vision of emaciated and flea-ridden strays came into her mind. 'I think I have enough to do at the moment, thank you, Jack,' she said. 'Perhaps later . . .'

'When the war's over and your brother can come out of hiding.'

She nodded, sighed and then went to the larder to find some food for him.

'What are you going to do with him?'

'With Alex?'

'Nah, with the dog, with Ben.'

Harriet realised that she hadn't even thought about it. They had no garden to bury him in, only a small paved yard at the back.

'I'll bury 'im for yer,' said Jack, standing up. 'What about in the gardens?' He pointed towards the front door.

'In the square you mean? Oh, I don't think the neighbours would like that.' But she realised as she spoke that it was the only solution and it wasn't as if anyone had bothered to tidy the garden in the square since the council no longer did it.

'Will you help me, Jack? I'll pay you for your work.'

Lifting Ben out of his bed brought a new surge of sadness but she let the tears flow freely down her cheeks since her hands were full. Jack had opened the door first and they had wrapped the body in an old sheet and together carried it across the road and through the gate into the square. The only thing they could find to dig the hole with was a small shovel used for the coal but Jack got to work energetically in a corner under a small oak tree while Harriet stood and watched, hoping that Alex would not come downstairs at this moment. She must protect him from further grief while his mental state was so delicate. If Ben had been anyone's dog in particular, he had been Alex's. Of course he would quickly notice the dog's absence so she had to choose the right time to break it to him.

Thinking of Alex made her look across towards the house and in doing so she noticed a figure at the window next door and shuddered. Their little task was being observed by Henry Carpian. Harriet tried to pretend that she hadn't seen him by helping Jack lower the dog into its grave.

When the deed was done they went back into

the house where Harriet gave Jack his parcel of food and a sixpenny piece.

'Will you do little jobs for me sometimes, Jack? I'll pay you of course.'

''Course I will, lady.'

'You can call me Harriet.'

''Arriet.' He savoured the word and then nodded, took the parcel of food and turned for the door.

Alex had had a bad night and was still sleeping when she looked in on him a few minutes later. This seemed to be the pattern of it now. The nightmares occurred around two or three o'clock and then he would fall into a deep sleep until around nine but the sleep never really refreshed him. His days varied from his being totally lucid and full of guilt to being far away in his mind and hardly responding to her at all.

There was one thing which was obvious. He was not getting any better. How long she would be able to cope was something she tried not to think about, since there was no alternative.

Gwen had visited once, but since her father had been reported missing she stayed at home to support her mother, who was not coping at all well. Another worrying thing was that a letter had arrived from Aunt Molly. Although her house was habitable, the east coast had suddenly become a less desirable place to live since that was where a lot of the bombing was taking place. Although London was also being hit she had hinted at coming back since both she and Harriet were alone. Harriet was at her wit's end thinking of an excuse to deter the dear and well-meaning woman from arriving. To expect Aunt Molly to keep a secret was like trying to hold water in a sieve. She spoke before she thought.

Temporarily the problem was taken care of – at least that's what Harriet hoped. Gwen had promised to write and explain that Harriet was taking up some war work and would be away from home. They'd even considered ambulance driving but had decided to be vague rather than lie outright. Of course, Aunt Molly might still choose to come and live in the London house alone but at least she had been stalled for a while. Being a person of sudden impulse, she might well just turn up on the doorstep.

When Alex shambled downstairs just after eleven o'clock he was unshaven and pale except for the red rims around his eyes. Harriet made him some breakfast and he picked at it in silence and hardly seemed to acknowledge her presence, let alone Ben's absence. She noticed a slight tremor in his hands as he lifted the cup of tea to his lips.

When the telephone rang he jumped and the

tea slopped all over the table. His eyes darted about nervously until Harriet laid a calming hand on his. 'It's just the telephone, Alex.'

She knew who it was and wondered why she was even answering it but anything was better than him arriving in person.

'Not your brother you were burying in the square I assume?' he said. 'That would be too good for him.'

Harriet felt an ice cold anger rise up. 'My brother has been at the front for the best part of fours years, Mr Carpian. He is injured just as you are but in his mind rather than his body.'

He laughed. 'Four years avoiding bullets? Either he's blessed with a guardian angel or he's been very clever at hiding in a dugout or tunnel. Do you know how long the life expectancy of a soldier is?'

'He was a medical orderly.'

'Ah, of course.'

'Was there anything else, Mr Carpian?'

'Since you have reminded me, yes. Medical orderlies carry morphia in their kits, do they not? You might bring round his supply please. I'm running low.'

Harriet's hand was shaking as she put down the telephone and replaced the earpiece on its hook. He's evil, evil, she thought. What was going to happen when the morphia ran out? But she knew already. He would send her out to a pharmacy to talk them into selling her some, or perhaps get Alex to write a prescription.

Her mind in a whirl, she went up to Alex's room and looked around for his kit bag. Then she remembered that he had taken it to his hiding place in the loft when the police came.

In the dark space under the eaves she found the bag and reached inside, feeling for the familiar box and syringes. She hated herself for it but what else could she do? Carpian was just waiting for the chance to report them to the police. There was no calling his bluff. He would carry it out and enjoy it but he obviously enjoyed this more. The rewards were twofold, the effects of the morphia and the feeling of power, the delight in seeing her obey his commands as instantly as soldiers had done.

Leaving the front door open, Harriet stepped along the pavement and up to his front door. He responded to her knock immediately and as she wordlessly handed over the items he opened the door wider.

'Come in,' he said with a sweep of his arm.

eleven

'No, thank you.' She turned to go but he grasped her wrist.

'What's the matter? Don't you find me attractive? Do you despise me for my habit?' He held up the morphia.

'I do not know you, Mr Carpian.' She tried to shake his hand away but he held on. 'Please let go before I call for help.'

He looked mockingly up and down the deserted street. 'I think your cries would be in vain, Miss Baker, or may I call you Harriet? We are neighbours after all, as well as having this closer relationship. Now please come in so we can discuss it inside rather than on the doorstep.'

Harriet reluctantly stepped inside his hall,

feeling she had no choice. Perhaps she was over-reacting. Despicable he may be but she must make allowances for the way war changed people. She must try and be civil.

He showed her into the parlour and asked her to sit down. At least it was clean and there was the pleasant scent of roses from a large bowl in the centre of a small table. Either he had a good housekeeper or he was a very unusual man.

Carpian sat opposite her. He was a big man with a well-shaped head and thick, dark brown hair. Certainly handsome. He glanced into the package. Then he looked up and met her eyes with his steely grey ones. 'This will do well for a short time but we must discuss the obtaining of further supplies.'

'Your addiction will require more and more of the drug,' she said, 'until at last you will not be satisfied. It is a poison, Mr Carpian, and will kill you.'

'Ah, there speaks the doctor's daughter,' he said. 'But I do not need your advice on how to live my life or how to die. The war has ruined what chances I had of a normal life and unlike your brother's so-called illness, there is no recovery.'

'I'm sorry.'

He pointed to his abdomen. 'Since you are acquainted with medical terminology I shall explain. I was shot badly in the gut, the result being a permanent colostomy. Can you imagine any young lady's reaction when she saw that?' he began pulling his shirt out of his trousers.

Harriet stood up. 'I do not need to see it either, Mr Carpian. I have seen them before . . .'

He stood up too and roughly pulled her to him. 'Then perhaps we should get to know each other better. It's a long time since I've held a woman . . .'

Harriet struggled to free herself but not before he had run his hands down her body.

He laughed bitterly. 'Perhaps next time you will remove your corset before you come here.'

'There will not be a next time.'

'Oh, but I think there may. The morphia is one thing but there may be other ways you can ensure that I do not reveal your secret.'

Harriet ran from the house and into her own, again leaning against the front door trying to recover from her ordeal. If only Father hadn't died now, if only Alex had returned to the front, if only she had never had to get tangled up with someone as brutish and inhuman as Henry Carpian. She was a strong woman, wasn't she? She had always thought so, but the events which were cropping up in her life were way beyond her experience. She longed for someone to turn to, to confide in, but apart from Gwen there was no-one. As a child growing up there had always been

Aunt Molly to turn to but this time she was on her own. She had outgrown Aunt Molly's advice and was venturing out into adult life on her own, as ultimately everyone was.

The darkness was just lifting when Alex opened his eyes. The silence just before dawn had been the same in the front lines as the men tried to rest before the coming battle. Just a cough here and there, a murmured prayer, the glow of a cigarette.

He remembered the birds beginning their dawn chorus though God knew where they were, there had been no trees just a bleak, flattened landscape of mud.

Alex listened to the stirrings of the first birds. The nightmares had been vivid again, so vivid that they stayed with him most of the day.

Despite being in his warm bed he was back with the men in the trenches, preparing for battle with the enemy as if it was some horrible game. It was set to start at seven-thirty and, like a ball game, would begin with the blow of a whistle.

Instead of the referee, the officer in charge stood with his pocket watch in his hand, watching as the seconds ticked away, bringing the whistle to his lips. Then the men would swarm over the parapet into no man's land while Alex and his comrades in the RAMC waited with dressings and morphia and stretchers to collect the dead and wounded.

It was after one such battle that he had met Patrick Burden. Jack, the boy who had broken into the house, reminded him of Patrick, and wasn't much younger. As they were returning with a wounded soldier they had found him crouching beside the remains of another young soldier, cradling his head in his arms and swaying to and fro, moaning gently.

Alex had stopped beside him, still grasping the two front handles of the stretcher.

'He's dead, lad. Come with us, you're in great danger here.'

The boy made no sign that he had heard but continued to rock backwards and forwards, a strange moaning, crooning sound escaping from his mouth.

Alex glanced back at the other orderly and they continued on with the stretcher and after delivering him to the regimental first aid post, the two men returned to the boy and gently lifted him up, prising the body from his arms.

He let out a cry and reached out. 'Laurie!'

'Your friend is dead,' said Alex again. 'We'll bring him back too.'

The boy turned his head and looked at him with a flash of defiance. 'He's my brother! I have to get Mother. She'll know what to do.'

He struggled to be free and the two men had to half carry him back to the trenches. He was in no fit state to fight but he was not injured either. There was nothing they could do but deliver him back to his comrades.

'We'll take care of him,' said one soldier. 'Poor little sod. He's only fifteen. Wanted to follow his big brother and fight for his country. They're just children.'

Alex struggled to escape his thoughts and swung his legs out of bed. He was living inside his head too much and it was an effort to stay in reality for long. Thoughts and images crowded his mind, pushing for prominence, as if there was limited space and sooner or later something would have to give. He knew that. He could feel pressure building like steam in a boiler and it terrified him.

Harriet was aware of it too, in fact her whole existence was like walking on eggshells. She took each day at a time, wondering when Alex would reach the crisis he seemed to be heading towards, when Henry Carpian would be back to force her to get him more morphia and when the police would spring a surprise visit and catch them out.

She had found the time to write to Aunt

Molly and dissuade her from coming, mentioning the increasing spread of the Spanish influenza epidemic. She allowed herself a small smile as she imagined her aunt's reaction. She would have an answer to that, even if the world's authorities didn't.

The morphia lasted Carpian two weeks. It was a Wednesday morning when he knocked on the door and fortunately not a day when she was expecting Jack. Harriet took a deep breath, pushed an escaped wisp of hair back round a hairpin, and went to the front door.

He didn't wait to be asked in but just stepped past her and she followed him into the surgery, her heart thudding. There was no more morphia in the house. What was he going to ask of her? Whatever else his desires were, he needed the drug more, but he could ask anything of her, couldn't he? That was the thing with blackmail, once you gave in the first time the price could continue increasing.

He was sitting at her father's desk, in his chair, with his legs crossed and she hated him for it. Whatever else he did, mocking her father's memory was far worse.

'Please say what you have come to say and leave.' She tried to keep her temper knowing he was doing it to taunt her.

He smiled and she briefly thought what a

waste it was that such a handsome man should be so evil.

He opened a drawer and took out a small notepad and she knew what it was. Her father's prescription pad. He pushed it across the desk towards her. Then, as if having second thoughts, he drew it towards him, removed the lid on the ink, dipped in a pen and began to write. Then he tore off the page and thrust it at her.

'I've made it very simple,' he said. 'All Alex has to do is sign.'

'And you are going to take it to the pharmacy?'

'Oh no, *you* are going to, my dear Harriet, while I wait here.'

He looked her over and she was aware of her demeaning position standing in front of the desk while he issued the orders.

'You look most attractive when you are angry,' he said. 'And I admire your courage.' When he saw that she hesitated to pick up the prescription, he stood up and came round to the front of the desk.

'I see that you *do* find me attractive,' he whispered, reaching out to touch her face.

'No! I do not! You . . . you repulse me. You are vile, Mr Carpian.' Harriet snatched up the prescription and hurried to the door, leaving him chuckling softly behind her.

She was not going to bother Alex. For a start, he would question her need for morphia. She had planned to mention an old patient, perhaps with recurrent acute pain or some such story, but who was going to administer the injection? He would be suspicious and would most certainly refuse even if he wasn't totally lucid.

Harriet forged her father's signature, but she was not going to tell Carpian that fact. Leaving him in the surgery she put on her coat and hat and went out.

It was October and the leaves in the square were changing, some had even begun to fall. She thought of Ben as she crossed the road and passed the oak tree under which he was buried. How she missed that dog. He would have brought her a little bit of comfort in her anxious days.

The pharmacist nearest to home had known her father well, it was where he had obtained all his medication, so she avoided that shop and went to another in Kensington High Street.

When she handed over the prescription the pharmacist looked at her over his spectacles.

'I'm his daughter,' she said. 'I help him in his practice. I was shopping and . . .' Don't be too liberal with explanations, she thought. She smiled. 'It's to replenish his stock. All these wounded soldiers we see these days . . .'

The pharmacist grimly smiled back and

nodded. 'I expect he's very busy.' When he handed over the package, Harriet smiled with relief. This time she had done it but how many times could she get away with it?

Carpian was reading one of the medical books off the shelf when she got back. Harriet was thankful at least to see that Alex had not yet come down. One of these days he would and she had no idea how she was going to explain Carpian's presence.

He was showing some signs of agitation and obviously needed to feed his habit so he wasted no time in grabbing the box and leaving. No embraces or fondling today, she thought, relaxing. Live one day at a time. Don't think too far ahead or worry about what might happen in the future.

Gwen came to visit several days later. There was still no news about her father and her mood was very low, so Harriet did not want to burden her with her own troubles.

'How is Alex?' she asked, sipping her cup of tea. It was ten o'clock and he was not yet down.

'He's not good. I'm really worried about him. The nightmares are getting more vivid and listening to his cries is heartbreaking.' She looked at her friend earnestly. 'Gwen, we just don't know what hell they are going through out there.'

She watched the pain cross Gwen's eyes as she nodded. 'People have no idea . . .' she whispered. Harriet reached out and covered Gwen's hand with her own.

'I'm sorry to hear about Ben.' Gwen looked over to the spot where the dog's bed had been. 'How did Alex take it?'

Harriet sighed. 'I broke it to him in a fairly lucid moment and he cried. That dog was his, you know. They grew up together. It's just one more loss he has to cope with. This war is certainly testing us to the limits.'

'I must get back to Mother.' Gwen stood up. 'It was lovely seeing you, Harriet. Thanks for the tea.' She frowned and pressed her fingers into her temples.

'Are you all right?'

Gwen shook her head. 'Just a headache, and the sniffles, I'll be fine.'

At that moment Harriet had a terrible premonition which took away her breath. When she could speak again she said, 'It's not the Spanish influenza, is it?'

Gwen grinned. 'Just too much worry,' she said, 'and not enough sleep.'

All of which lowers resistance to infection, thought Harriet as she opened the front door.

twelve

Alex stared at the prisoner being dragged out. This was one of the hardest duties he'd had to perform, being the medical officer present at an execution. He stood to the side, watching the poor lad stumble towards the post, half carried by two soldiers. It looked as if they'd got him drunk to blur the reality of what was happening to him.

Suddenly Alex went cold. He *knew* the lad. It was the one he'd found crouching over the body of his older brother in no man's land. Half off his head with grief and scared rigid. He was only fifteen! He'd been there, exposed, not fearing for himself but wanting to help his brother. He was no coward.

Alex remembered that the only words he had

heard him speak was calling for his mother. They couldn't do this! Now his mother would have lost two sons, and one would have inadvertently brought shame on the family. Whatever had he done? Refused to go over the top? Run in terror the wrong way? Hidden in a dugout?

Nausea swept over Alex as he watched the boy being tied to the post. He glanced down at the trial schedule. Patrick Alan Burden. Found guilty of desertion on July 10th 1918. Of no further military value. Commander-in-Chief, Field Marshall Douglas Haig had signed 'confirmed' to the recommendation of the death penalty.

At a command from the Captain the firing squad marched out and positioned themselves in a line facing the prisoner, rifles on their shoulders.

As the blindfold was about to be tied the boy shook his head, his mouth set, eyes darting about with terror. He shook from head to toe and small moaning sounds escaped his lips, yet he had the courage to face his executioners.

Alex was transfixed. He felt dead inside, his heart like stone. He didn't want to watch yet seemed compelled. He wanted to call out but knew he could not change the situation but would only prolong it. There was no changing the court's decision. There never was.

Another cry and a movement in the ranks caught his eye. One of the soldiers in the firing squad had dropped to the ground in a faint. Alex ran forward just as the Captain yelled, 'Get him out!' He placed his hands under the soldier's arms and dragged him out of the line. The Captain was obviously impatient to get on with it, rapping his stick against his leg.

The soldier was beginning to come round but was in no fit state to continue. Alex felt, rather than saw, the Captain leaning over. He could hear the snapping of the stick. Then a rifle was thrust under his nose.

'We need twelve. You can replace him, Lieutenant.'

Alex was speechless with horror as he slowly stood up, staring at the officer in front of him.

'I'm a medical orderly, a doctor, Sir.'

'I'm well aware of that. Not a Quaker are you?'

Without thinking, Alex shook his head.

'And I'm sure you can fire a rifle? Let's get on with it, then.'

The rifle was heavy and cold in his hands. Alex stared down at it, feeling numb as he took the soldier's place in the line. As if in slow motion he pulled back the bolt.

'Ready!'

Rifles to shoulders. Take aim. Watch the Captain as he raises his stick.

Alex felt sick.

'Tell yourself yours is the blank one,' whispered the man next to him.

The stick fell.

thirteen

Gwen went down the steps, swayed, grasped hold of the railings and fell to her knees. Harriet ran out and caught her and together they managed to get back inside.

'I'll be all right,' Gwen said after she'd been sitting in an armchair in the parlour for five minutes. She struggled to her feet again but was obviously in no state to go anywhere.

Harriet felt her forehead. It was burning. She went into the surgery for a thermometer and put it under Gwen's tongue.

'Well?' Gwen asked after the three minutes were up and Harriet was studying the mercury level.

'It's a hundred and four point two,' said

Harriet. 'I'm going to make up Father's bed in the surgery. You can't go home, Gwen. I'll get word to your mother and look after you here.'

She could see that Gwen was not going to argue and that in itself proved how ill she was feeling.

By the next morning she had the tell-tale bluish tinges around her ears and was only half aware of her surroundings. Harriet had her propped up with pillows to help her breathe and had given her an inhalation to try and clear her airways.

When Jack came she sent him to Gwen's house with a message for her mother telling her to try not to worry and that Harriet would do her best for Gwen. There was not a lot anyone could do and she knew that the hospitals were bursting with returning wounded soldiers and flu patients.

When there was a knock at the front door she thought it was Jack returning and quickly washed her hands and went to open it, towel in hand.

The two policemen stood on the doorstep again. Harriet was totally unprepared. She had thought that they may return but other things had taken up her attention. Now she stared at them with a sinking feeling and felt the colour drain from her face and a slight dizziness caused her to grip the door frame.

'May we come in, Miss Baker?' asked the

senior officer. 'We are not entirely happy with our search the other week.'

She didn't know whether or not Alex was up but he certainly would not have had the presence of mind to hide every time there was a knock at the door.

The younger policeman made a move to push past her arm.

'No,' she said. 'You can't come in.'

He grinned in triumph and spoke for the first time. 'We have a warrant, remember?'

'So you may,' she said, 'and you are welcome to come in but I should tell you that the influenza is here. I am nursing a friend who is ill.'

Both policemen took a step back but then the older one smiled, not maliciously but with a certain knowing look. 'Clever, Miss Baker, but we weren't born yesterday.'

She held his gaze. 'I am not lying. My friend is Gwen Hill and if you don't believe me, go and ask her mother. She lives in Church Street, Number six.'

She could see that they were uncertain now and there was apprehension in their eyes.

'I must get back to her,' said Harriet. 'If you'll excuse me.' She stepped back and closed the door knowing that the policemen were not going to risk being infected by this lethal disease. The chances of survival were low and each day it claimed hundreds more lives.

Harriet had tried to make sure that Alex came nowhere near Gwen and she herself had taken extreme precautions to ensure that she did not carry any infection out of the sickroom. As soon as she entered the room she donned a large apron which wrapped around her and which remained in the room when she left. She washed her hands thoroughly in disinfectant, burnt Gwen's handkerchiefs and boiled the cup and bowl used to feed her copious fluids and soup.

She had asked Jack to come every day to run errands for her but she would not allow him in the house, fearing that he would take the disease back to his already undernourished family. Instead she gave instructions through the letter box and dropped disinfected coins into his hands.

By the third day Gwen had not reached the crisis and Harriet began to wonder if there was anything else she could be doing. She got out some of her father's text books but this Spanish flu was a new strain, which was why it was proving so deadly throughout the world. It had already claimed more lives than the whole of the war.

As Harriet looked down at her friend, tears sprang into her eyes. Was she going to lose her too? Immediately she felt ashamed. What of Gwen's mother who had probably lost her husband and also had a son away at war?

She heard a horse stop outside and peeked through the curtains. A man was descending from a hansom. It was certainly not the police. He was not in uniform and besides, the police did not use horse transport.

Harriet quickly took off her apron and washed her hands and then went to open the door.

He was quite tall with light brown hair. When he smiled his eyes crinkled up and exuded warmth. The smile was short-lived however.

'Miss Baker?'

'Yes.' She was wary. Was this some other authority coming to look for Alex?

'I'm Ken Winterton,' he said. 'A doctor friend of your brother's. You telephoned me some time ago. I was passing and wondered . . . if you had had any news?'

He spoke quietly with a gentle and reassuring manner and never took his eyes off her face. Suddenly he was the answer to everything. She did not know him but felt she could trust him. She had to have help, had to confide in someone. Here was a friend of Alex's, and if he were a true friend . . . and he was a doctor, treating patients with the flu. Since he looked healthy, though tired, he must have built up an immunity, being around them all the time. Did she have a right to burden him further?

'Please come in,' she said.

He stepped into the hall and she closed the door and showed him into the parlour. She watched as he wrinkled up his nose.

'My friend has the flu but I have tried to contain the infection in the surgery.'

He took the proffered seat, shaking his head. 'Don't worry about me. But what about yourself?'

'I feel well enough,' she said. 'But Doctor Winterton . . .'

'Please call me Ken,' he interrupted.

'Ken, I . . .'

He frowned a little, although not with irritation but rather concentration. It must be a frequent habit as she noticed little lines across his brow and at the outer edges of his eyes.

'I'm risking a lot but I feel I can trust you.'

He nodded, urging her to continue. She couldn't believe she was about to divulge a secret to this stranger which could affect her dear brother's life, but all of a sudden the burden of it was more than she could bear.

'What are your feelings about shell-shock?'

Winterton nodded slowly and sat back in the chair. 'It is as much an injury as any physical one,' he said. 'And in some cases may be more devastating. Only time will tell. I assume you are asking me this because Alex is suffering?'

Harriet nodded.

'Where is he? Have you heard from him recently? Is he being treated?'

'He is here,' Harriet said, quietly, and for the next fifteen minutes told the doctor everything that had happened from the moment her father had stopped his diet.

Once she left to see to Gwen, she returned to find Winterton hadn't moved at all but was sitting staring into the fireplace.

'We were great chums in med school.'

She nodded. 'He spoke of you, although we never met.'

'Miss Baker . . .' He rose from his chair, at the same time taking out his pocket watch and flipping the lid. 'I must get back to the hospital but I'll be back. I'd like to speak to Alex – and, of course, your secret is safe with me. He is in no fit state to fight. I will take a look at your friend before I leave, though.'

Again, she was grateful for his professional advice, although he really had none to give, but congratulated her on how well she was caring for Gwen.

'She should reach the crisis soon,' he said, 'and she's young. She has probably more chance of recovery than many.'

This time when Harriet closed the front door, her sigh of relief was for an entirely different reason. Her heart felt lighter than it had for a long time and she realised she hadn't even offered the man a cup of tea.

Then the telephone rang.

fourteen

Alex shivered as he got out of bed. The sun was pouring in through his bedroom window as he drew back the curtains but there was a definite October chill in the air and the trees in the square were beginning to turn yellow.

His legs felt shaky as he went out to the bathroom and the pressure inside his skull thumped painfully. It seemed as if his chest was constricted so that breathing was an effort and something was trying to burst out.

He splashed cold water on his face, his mind drifting from Harriet downstairs to the men outside in the trenches. Another day. More orders. More needless slaughter. Poor Harriet, trying to cope and looking after Gwen too. He would go and see if he could be of some use. Too much of being cooped up alone in his room was not good. Morale had to be maintained. That's how fighting armies were kept on their toes.

Strangely, he couldn't find his uniform so he put on a cotton shirt and a pair of flannel trousers. Take it easy on the stairs. Just one at a time. Don't fall. Legs like jelly. A sound came from the parlour. A muffled cry. He increased his pace, stumbling on the last stair and grabbing the newel post to stop himself falling.

The door was closed and he grasped the handle and pushed it open. Harriet was in the arms of a strange man. He was leaning over her trying to kiss her and her blouse was torn and pulled down off her shoulders. The man had his hand inside it and on her breast and she was pushing him away, shaking her head and struggling to free herself.

At that moment the man half turned and saw Alex. He showed no surprise but smiled slightly although his eyes were dead. Alex had seen eyes like that before. Cold, ruthless eyes, which showed no mercy, whose owners were incapable of warmth.

Surprising himself at his speed, Alex leapt forward and grasped the man's collar, dragging him off Harriet. Then, in one fluid movement, he drew back his fist and punched the man's cold eyes.

His victim cried out, let go of Harriet and, grasping his face, staggered backwards off balance, and fell heavily into the marble hearth. There he lay still, blood streaming from his split scalp.

Harriet had quickly recovered herself and was staring from Alex to the man in horror.

'Oh Alex,' she said.

'Who is he?'

'Our neighbour, Henry Carpian. Oh my God, he's unconscious.' She was trying to pull her torn blouse across while staring at the man lying on the floor.

'What's he doing here?'

'He found out about you, Alex. He threatened to inform the authorities. He's been blackmailing me.'

Alex was horrified. Surely not . . . ?

She saw the way his thoughts were going and shook her head. 'He's addicted to morphia and has been blackmailing me for supplies.' She saw the way he was nursing his knuckles. 'Oh, you've hurt your hand.'

Alex had suddenly become aware of the pain of his right hand from impacting with Carpian's bony eye socket and he flexed his fingers carefully. 'I'm all right, but what are we going to do with him?'

Harriet looked back at the still figure on the

floor and Alex could see the mixed emotions on his sister's face. She was basically a caring person yet had reason to hate this man, and to fear him. Now, more than ever, they were in great danger from him. He would not let this attack go with impunity.

Alex's mind was crystal clear and was focussed on one thing. They must get Carpian back to his own house and make it look like an accident, as if he had fallen and cracked his head on his own hearth while under the influence of morphia.

'You've purchased morphia for him before?'

'When Father's supplies ran out, yes.'

'You must go out and get more. Go to a different pharmacy. I'll write you a prescription on Father's paper. If this devil wants morphia, he shall have it.'

Harriet hesitated, obviously trying to get her mind round what he was planning. Alex knelt and felt for Carpian's pulse.

'He's alive?'

He nodded, looking up at her. 'His pulse is weak. I suspect he may have fractured his skull when he fell.'

Still she stood, looking down at them both. Then she scanned the room and he read her mind.

'He's not staying here. We'll take him back

next door, give him some morphia and then telephone for an ambulance. Say we heard a cry. They must think that he fell as a result of the morphia.'

He could see that she was uneasy about the plan, yet what choice did they have? '*You* must say you heard his cry,' he corrected.

Harriet nodded. 'I'll just look in on Gwen.'

He'd forgotten about Gwen for the moment. Harriet left the room and he heard the murmur of her voice before the front door opened and closed. Then he went upstairs to the linen cupboard and found a clean towel to wrap around Carpian's head to prevent leaving a trail of blood.

The man was heavy and Alex was weak. He dragged him into the hall and to the front door and then opened it and stepped outside. The cool fresh smell of autumn bathed his face and he took a deep breath. It was good to be outside again.

It was close to noon and no-one was about. Next door was not far but it was going to take him a minute or two at least to drag the man round there. There was no question of being able to put him over his shoulder. Perhaps he ought to wait for Harriet's return. But she would hate this. It went right against her nature to treat someone like this. He, however, had no such qualms. He'd had to learn to be impartial, it had been his job.

It was only when he had got the inert Carpian

to his own porch, that he realised the door was closed. He should have opened it first, and what if someone else was in the house? He hadn't thought of that.

Rummaging in the man's pocket produced a key. Alex was breathing heavily now, both from exertion and nervousness. It only needed someone to come round the corner, a vehicle to pass, someone to come out of their front door, and he would be caught. He was both a deserter and now perhaps a murderer, if Carpian did not survive.

With a shaking hand he managed to insert the key in the lock and turn it. The door opened and despite the need for haste, he stopped to listen. Silence.

When he had the man in his own parlour he took off the towel and let the body fall on his own hearth, cringing at the crack it made as the head hit the hard surface for the second time. Blood was still flowing so he was still alive. Alex refrained from feeling the pulse again.

What should he do now? Wait here for Harriet or go home and then come back with her? If Carpian was discovered in the meantime it would still look like an accident.

'Hello?' A man's voice from the still open front door. Alex froze.

'Anyone home? Parcel to sign for.'

Alex tried to compose himself. 'Just a minute.' He rolled up the bloody towel and put it next to Carpian, then looked down at himself. No blood.

'It's a bit risky to leave your front door open these days, Sir,' said the postman as Alex scribbled a signature and took the small package out of the postman's hand. He nodded and tried to smile but the postman was already back to his cart on the footpath. Wasn't their front door open too? That would seem strange. But there was fortunately no post for them today and the postman didn't even glance at the house.

Alex remembered to take Carpian's key and closed his front door but then saw Harriet turn the corner.

Together they knelt over the inert form in the hearth. Alex drew up the morphia solution in the syringe and dispelled the air while Harriet straightened out the man's arm and tightened the tourniquet they'd found lying on the table awaiting his next fix. Carpian moaned and pulled a face but didn't open his eyes.

The strain of the whole thing was beginning to tell on Alex as he felt for a vein in Carpian's arm. The man was in poor shape and no good veins presented themselves. His hand shook and the needle hovered just above the skin. If he couldn't find a vein he would have to inject it into the muscle but the effect would be slower.

Then Harriet's hand was on his, guiding the needle in. He withdrew a little to make sure it was in a vein and when blood appeared in the syringe he pushed the plunger home.

Putting the door key on the hall table, they left, looking both ways up the street before hurrying back to their own house, where Harriet sank into a chair, her face chalk white.

Then she looked up at Alex. 'I never thought we would sink to this,' she said.

'He brought it on himself. Now you must telephone an ambulance. Say you knew Carpian wasn't well and heard a crash and a cry. When you banged on his front door there was no reply.'

Harriet stared at him, reluctant to compound her lies even further.

'*You* have to do it, Harriet. I can't.'

fifteen

The influenza developed very quickly into a vicious type of pneumonia which left the patient gasping for breath and blue through lack of oxygen. Harriet had kept Gwen propped upright to aid her breathing and regularly gave her inhalations. When her fever rose to critical levels she tried to reduce it by bathing her constantly in tepid water.

On the evening of the incident with Henry Carpian, Gwen reached her crisis.

By now she was delirious and Harriet sat on the bed watching her friend fight for her life. Losing Gwen would be the final cruel blow. In the last few months she had had as much as she could handle, more stress and grief than many people had in a lifetime. Until now when she had reached this depth of despair, she would remember that so many people were suffering, she had no right to think hers was any worse, but everyone had their breaking point and Harriet knew that hers was close and that, like a drowning person, she would soon have to draw that fatal breath from which there was no return.

She held Gwen's hot, sticky hand in hers for a moment longer and then gently laid it on the sheet and stood up. While Gwen still lived, she must find the strength from somewhere. It was time she gave her friend another cool sponge down.

Alex had gone upstairs again, his moments of lucidity while he dealt with Carpian had faded. Now his mind was back with his comrades in the trenches.

The telephone rang, making Harriet jump and her heart race. Then she felt a guilty relief as she realised that Carpian was not capable of tormenting her from his hospital bed.

She lifted the telephone and put the earpiece to her ear.

Out of habit she almost said 'Dr Baker's practice' and then in confusion could only manage 'Hello'.

It was the hospital. Carpian was dead. There would be a post-mortem but X-rays showed that he had fractured his skull when he fell. They suspected some sort of drug in his body, would she have any idea what he was taking?

'I hardly knew him,' she said. 'I'm sorry I can't help.'

One weight had lifted from her shoulders. She had never thought she would ever be relieved over someone's death. Would there be an investigation, an inquest? The post-mortem would reveal his high level of morphia and confirm the skull fracture. It would be straightforward, wouldn't it? Was there any reason for anyone to suspect she had lied?

Harriet picked up the bowl of water and continued to the surgery. That she could worry about later. Now Gwen needed her.

She felt a surge of emotion choke her as she dipped the sponge in the lukewarm water and gently dabbed Gwen's pale face mottled with blue. Tears welled up in her eyes. Tears which had been held back, unshed, for so long now. If she let go, there would be no stopping them.

The rattling in Gwen's chest seemed worse and each breath was such a tremendous effort that Harriet feared her friend would soon be too exhausted to carry on.

'Please, Gwen,' she whispered, squeezing out the sponge and reapplying it to her friend's brow, 'don't leave me now. I need your strength.'

There was no response from Gwen and she hadn't expected any. Later when she tried to force some water between her lips, the swallowing reflex was barely present.

All day Harriet tended to her friend, watching for any sign that her crisis was over, for either improvement or deterioration. Once Alex opened the door and looked in but came no further. His eyes were clear and met hers, then went to the figure on the bed. He raised his eyebrows questioningly and she shook her head. Five minutes later he returned with a cup of tea and a sandwich for her, leaving them on a table just inside the door. Dear, thoughtful Alex. The tears welled up again.

It was ten o'clock that evening when Gwen's condition changed. The clammy skin seemed warmer and breathing marginally easier. At first Harriet thought it was her imagination or wishful thinking. She rubbed her eyes, fatigued almost to the point of passing out, and reached for the thermometer.

There was some improvement, albeit slight. Fetching a blanket, Harriet wrapped it around herself and settled down to sleep in the chair beside the bed. She could hardly keep her eyes open and was aware of her mind wandering bizarrely. She would be no good to anyone if she collapsed with fatigue.

At some time in the early hours Gwen's movement awoke Harriet and she gazed into her friend's open eyes.

'Harriet.' The word was faint and difficult through cracked lips despite Harriet's bathing them with glycerine. She sprung from the chair and gently hugged her friend, who tried to push her away, fearful of spreading the infection.

But Harriet was laughing and shaking her head, the pent-up emotions of the previous evening turned to those of happiness and relief.

Gwen was going to live.

Some of Harriet's relief touched Alex and mixed confusingly with his darker moments. It was as if he were living two separate lives simultaneously, one here with his sister and Gwen and the other with his pals in the trenches. Often he experienced both these existences as if he were an onlooker watching a play, emotionally involved on a minor level but detached. Then he would be plunged back into the war experience in a heightened and overwhelming way, playing out the dreadful scenes over and over, embedding them more permanently in his subconscious.

A day or two after Gwen's crisis, he had lost track of time, the doorbell had penetrated his thoughts and, completely disregarding his own safety, he had gone to the top of the stairs to see who it was.

Harriet opened the door and he heard the low tones of a man's voice, for a moment being reminded of the incident with that other man, Carpian. Something bad had happened then which he couldn't quite recall, something to do with Harriet. He gripped the banister and started down the stairs, aware that Harriet had invited the man to enter.

'Alex!' Harriet had gasped. They were both looking up at him, she with an anxious expression on her face and he . . . he looked friendly and somehow familiar.

'Hello Alex, it's Ken. Ken Winterton.' The man had extended his hand and, out of habit, as Alex reached the hall, he took it.

'Ken?'

The man nodded. 'I hear you have had a rough time.' The eyes were full of concern. Alex followed them into the parlour.

'I'll make some tea,' Harriet said. 'I was very rude last time you came and didn't offer you anything.' Alex noticed the look of warmth that passed between them and the slight flush to Harriet's cheeks.

'How is your friend?' the man said, taking a seat.

'She is recovering, thank God.'

Winterton smiled. 'She is lucky. Not many do.' He was looking at Alex again.

'Ken Winterton.' Alex nodded slowly. 'Doctor Ken Winterton.'

Winterton laughed. 'You've got it, old chum.'

Harriet looked from one to the other and then left the room.

Looking at the now-familiar face brought others flooding in, fighting for space in his head, all wanting his attention. So many. So many now dead. So many he'd seen blown to pieces in front of him. How had he, Alex, escaped? What right had he to still be alive?

Alex realised that he had spoken out loud when he saw Winterton nod and lean forward, his brow lined with concern.

'So many gone,' said Alex. 'Slaughter. You have no idea.'

'I do,' said Winterton, softly. 'I haven't been there but I patch up their broken bodies and minds. Every day I hear the appalling stories.'

Another face was emerging. A face which had been wanting attention for some time now, vague, blurred. This face he didn't want to see. This face, more than all the others, threatened to stay and haunt him.

It was the face of a boy. Patrick Burden. The face had a name. He was fifteen years old.

'They made me do it,' whispered Alex. 'I was there to save lives not destroy them.'

He was aware of Harriet coming into the room quietly even though his mind was elsewhere. Someone urged him on and there could be no stopping now. The dam had burst. The unfolding of events could not be stopped. They had to come out at last.

He was back in that place, standing in a line of soldiers, rifles raised to shoulders, fingers on triggers. All barrels pointed at the target – a small figure tied to a post and staring at them with wild eyes. A figure which trembled from head to foot unable to hide his terror and down whose uniform trousers a slowly spreading stain showed his inability to control his bladder.

The Captain in charge of the firing squad raised his stick. When it fell, they were all to shoot the lad. One had a blank loaded in the breach. Would that person know? Was there a different feel to firing a live round or a blank? Alex had had almost no experience of firearms to tell one way or the other. One out of the twelve.

'He fell,' said Alex. 'The man fell.' He was aware of Harriet's intake of breath and wondered for a moment what she feared. All he could see was the soldier who had fainted. 'Passed out. He passed out. I had to replace him.'

The Captain's stick fell. Alex squeezed the

trigger and the rifle kicked. A volley of sound cracked the silence. Smoke and the smell of cordite filled the air. The figure had stopped shaking and had slumped as far as his bonds would allow. Unmoving. Still.

'No!' Alex cried out and felt hands grasp his. At the same time someone gave an order and the men in line with him turned and marched away. He could hear himself sobbing and it felt as though his energy and life were flowing away with the tears, leaving him empty.

'Pull yourself together!' barked the Captain, taking the rifle out of his hands, 'and do what you are here to do. Pronounce the man dead so that I can order a detail to bury him.'

Man? This had not been a man. Not yet. He had only been a boy. A boy who would never now reach manhood. Alex walked over to the inert body, aware that the officer had unholstered his revolver.

He reached forward and felt for the carotid pulse. There was none. To make sure, he took his stethoscope out of his pocket and listened to the boy's chest. Silence.

'There'll be no need for that,' he said. 'He's dead.'

'My God!' It was Harriet. He felt her arms around him. 'Why you, Alex?'

He was back with them now, at home.

'Because I was there,' he said, 'and they needed a twelfth man to fulfil the regulations. One had passed out.'

'You should sleep now, old chum,' said Winterton. 'I'll prescribe you a sedative.'

Alex willingly let himself be led upstairs to his room. The crushing sensation in his chest had gone and he felt lighter, having purged the horrible incident from his mind. There were many more he would never be rid of, but he was tired, so tired.

Winterton had brought his medical bag and Alex felt a prick in the arm and then the warm feeling of drowsiness the sedative induced.

Then he slept like a baby for the first time in months.

epilogue

On the eleventh of November the war ended but the influenza epidemic did not. Christmas had brought mixed blessings, Harriet thought as she washed the dinner dishes and listened to the voices in the other room.

The surgery had been reverted back into a dining room, as it had been originally designed to be. Alex had made some improvement although Ken said that he would probably never be quite free of the traumatic memories and their effects.

Gwen was well although still in convalescence. Her mother and father, the latter alive but having been wounded, had come to celebrate Christmas with them and Ken managed to take an hour away from the hospital to join them too. He was such a good friend and she attributed most of Alex's recovery to him, along with the attention Alex received from Gwen and which was beginning to be reciprocated.

Alex would have to face a court-martial and she hoped he would cope with the stress and that the penalty would not be too great. Again, Ken had said he would write a full report about Alex's state of mind at the time of the so-called desertion.

Aunt Molly was there too, her usual ebullient self and they were careful not to mention Alex's 'desertion' although she would find out soon enough.

The one event which would never come out was the truth about Henry Carpian's death. That was a burden which she – and Alex – would have to bear for the rest of their lives. Something they could never tell anyone.

Whether or not that burden would eventually become too great, only time would tell. But for now, peace was among them.

author's notes

The idea for this book has been with me for some time, although it has changed considerably, as ideas often do. It began when I visited the United States and heard about a woman who fought as a man in the Civil War. My initial plan was for Harriet to replace her brother at the front, posing as a man but I then realised that strength of character and loyalty to her brother would be required just as much if she remained at home and hid him from the authorities.

I have a great interest in the past, particularly social history. The end of the First World War was a great turning point, especially for women, with their emancipation, freedom and independence, the latter largely brought about by having to do men's work while they were away fighting.

Thank you for choosing this book and I hope you enjoyed reading it as much as I enjoyed writing it.

Facts you may be interested in:

- Until the discovery of insulin in 1921 by Dr Frederick Banting and Charles Best, the diagnosis of diabetes was a death sentence. In some cases diet could prolong life but inevitably what it amounted to was starvation.

- Alex may or may not have been shot as a deserter but he certainly would have faced a court-martial, even after the War was over. During World War One more than 20,000 servicemen were convicted by court-martial of offences which carried the death sentence. Of those, 3,000 were ordered to be put to death and just over ten percent of the executions were carried out. These 306 British and Commonwealth servicemen died by a firing squad made up of men from their own regiment; they appeared on no memorial and their widows received no war pension.

- Even though people knew about 'shell-shock' - what today we call Post Traumatic Stress Disorder - these soldiers were not given fair trials and were often not properly defended. It wasn't until 2006 that they were posthumously pardoned and a memorial erected.

book club questions
for discussion

1. The title of the book comes from the quote *"True strength is not a measure of the body, but a measure of the soul."* Discuss the meaning of this in terms of Harriet's problems.

2. Dr Baker has what we call today type 1 diabetes, i.e. a dependence on insulin to metabolise the carbohydrates ingested. Discuss what you know about the disease and what life must have been like in 1918 when someone was diagnosed.

3. Harriet has always had an uneasy relationship with her father. Why was this? Do you think she regrets those years? Why has it changed recently?

4. When Alex fails to return to the front before the end of his leave, do you think Harriet was morally right to hide him from the authorities or should he have gone back and faced the consequences?

5. Is there a case for soldiers being shot for desertion to deter others in time of war? How would you define desertion? Was the government right to posthumously pardon all those executed in World War I?

6. Discuss changes in the lives of women in World War I and immediately after.

7. What factors have caused Henry Carpian's bitterness? Discuss the reasons for the methods by which he blackmails Harriet.

8. When Carpian dies as a result of hitting his head after Alex punched him, were they right to cover it up or should they have admitted that it was accidental? Was Harriet doing this to save her own skin or that of her brother?

9. Main characters should learn from their experiences in the story and have developed and changed by the end. In what ways did Harriet change and mature?

10. There is comfort in routine. Perhaps it's a form of burying your head in the sand and warding off change which could upset the status quo. What routines does Harriet follow? Discuss routines – or even 'ruts' in your own life. At gatherings do you always sit in the same seat, for example? Are you compelled always to do things in the same order? What are we afraid of?

11. Aunt Molly is a good person and means well but sometimes there is a fine line between being thoughtful and compassionate and being domineering and inflexible. Discuss this type of character.

12. Alex and his father are very close. In what ways did Doctor Baker influence his son?

13. Because of media limitations at this time, the public was largely ignorant as to the enormity of the losses at the front. Should this be played down to keep up morale or do you think the public is entitled to the truth no matter how bad it is? What can be the result of that?

A Death in the Family

Caroline Dunford

I briefly considered the option of swooning in a ladylike manner, but I was denied this by virtue of position: I was a maid; and by natural inclination: I have never known how to swoon. Instead, I did what I believe most females of sensibility would have done finding themselves alone with a murdered corpse. I screamed exceedingly loudly, quite in the common manner, and pelted out of the room . . .

In December 1909 the Reverend Joshia Martins expires in a dish of mutton and onions leaving his family on the brink of destitution. Joshia's daughter, Euphemia, takes it upon herself to provide for her mother and little brother by entering service. She's young, fit, intelligent, a little naive and assumes the life of a maid won't be too demanding. However, on her first day at the unhappy home of Sir Stapleford she discovers a murdered body.

Euphemia's innate sense of justice has her prying where no servant should look and uncovering some of the darker secrets of the Stapleford family. All she has to defend herself with is her quick wits, sense of humour and the ultimate weapon of all virtuous young women, her scream.

Euphemia tells the tale in a light-hearted way, writing in a style akin to a cross between Jane Austen and Agatha Christie.

'A sparkling and witty crime debut with a female protagonist to challenge Miss Marple.'
Lin Anderson, Award winning Scottish crime author and screen writer

ISBN 978-1-905637-90-4   £6.99

PRINT
PUBLISHING

This Fragile Life

David Webb

Matt felt sick. He sank down onto a chair, the phone still clasped to his ear. He didn't speak for a few moments and Meg broke the silence.
'Are you still there, Matt? Are you all right? I thought you'd want to know.'
'Yes, thanks Meg. I'm coming in. I'm on my way.'
Matt put the phone down and sat still in the dark. Meg's words were echoing in his head and he was desperately trying to make sense of them . . .

Matthew Hudson is constantly reminded just how fragile life can be. Depressed by his routine existence in Manchester, Matt is haunted by the one failed relationship he has behind him – with Lydia, a dancer who left him to further her career in London. However, when he meets Laura, an attractive young primary school teacher, life seems to be looking up for Matt – until one phone call changes everything . . .

This Fragile Life is the first novel produced by prolific children's author David Webb.

ISBN 978-1-905637-87-4   £6.99

ePRINT
PUBLISHING

Missing Link

Elizabeth Kay

Spliff laughed softly. "Perhaps outright murder is the only thing we'll stop at on Missing Link. Because just when you all think it can't get any worse, it does . . ."

Jessica Pierce is a guest on the investigative chatshow *Missing Link*. The hugely popular programme is hosted by Spliff, a quick-thinking media-savvy presenter.
The show features two guests; they will never have met before. But a "heaven or hell" link between them is revealed – either something wonderful, such as a long-lost relative, or something appalling, like a false identity.
Spliff violently disapproves of the way television has been dumbed down and he decides to make a programme which will be so shocking that the series will be taken off the air, questions will be asked, and maybe television will be the better for it.
So when Spliff decides to go out with a bang, who will he take with him? . . .

"*Missing Link* teases you, tempts you to think you're as smart as the programme makers who manipulate, backbite and play out cut-throat rivalries behind the scenes. Just when you think you've got its measure—as tart satire on mass entertainment, as comedy of manners, even as romance—it opens a trapdoor on dizzying questions of science and morality. Like its enigmatic and dark-edged romantic lead, Elizabeth Kay's prescient novel layers its witty and intricate mind games with a heartfelt indignation, and even a hint of human vulnerability."
Philip Gross, Author

A skilled and ingenious piece of work
Fay Weldon, Author

ISBN 978-1-905637-88-1 £6.99

ePRINT

PUBLISHING

Spectacles

Pippa Goodhart

For days after that it was as if I'd died and gone to Heaven. The world was so full of beauty! . . . Seeing the world so clear felt like falling in love all over again . . .

When her domineering Mother dies, Iris is shocked by what she finds when clearing out her flat. It turns out that she is illegitimate. So Iris isn't the person she'd thought she was. Perhaps she can reinvent herself now?

When Iris acquires a pair of spectacles, she gains a renewed focus on life. She gives us her vision of the world around her, a clear, sometimes almost painfully comic view of people, places and the Meaning of Life! This complicated old woman shares some episodes from her life that move from gentle humour and pure farce to moments of tragedy and deep despair. Iris is always full of surprises, and she leaves the biggest surprise till the end of the novel, when she shocks the reader with the most poignant, eye-opening revelation of all.

Throughout this potpourri of a novel, Goodhart writes with humour and pathos as we follow this wonderful old woman [...] on an emotional journey.
Alan Wright, Author, nominated for *Debut Dagger* Award

A moving story of life, death and all the questions in between. Louise Heyden, Librarian

ISBN 978-1-905637-86-7   £6.99

PRINT
PUBLISHING